Ripley's®

Coral Colony Creatures

Written by:
Doug Perrine

with an Introduction by:
Joseph M. Choromanski

Original Art by:
Corena Ricks

Series Edited by:
Edward Meyer

SCHOLASTIC INC.

New York Toronto London Auckland Sydney
Mexico City New Delhi Hong Kong Buenos Aires

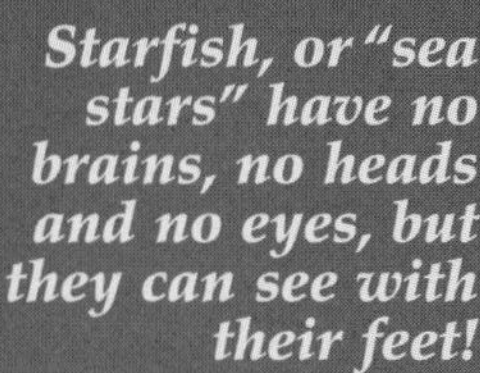

Starfish, or "sea stars" have no brains, no heads and no eyes, but they can see with their feet!

The "horns" of this opalescent nudibranch serve the colorful sea slug as organs of touch, smell and taste.

The Most Venomous Animal on Earth. The venom of the box jellyfish found in the waters off Australia, is so deadly it can kill a human in four minutes, yet hawksbill turtles regularly swallow the jellyfish without being harmed.

Coral Colony Creatures was designed by Infinite Ideas & Designs, Casselberry, Florida.

ISBN 0-439-34272-4

12 11 10 9 8 7 6 5 4 3 2 1 1 2 3 4 5 6/0

Printed in the U.S.A. 14

First Scholastic printing, December 2001

In the over 80 years Ripley's Believe It or Not! has been publishing cartoons, we have printed literally hundreds of facts about the thousands of invertebrate creatures that populate the coral colonies of the world. Ripley himself visited Australia's Great Barrier Reef, the Red Sea, and the reefs of the Caribbean—three of the most magnificent undersea regions of the world— and was clearly fascinated by the seemingly endless kinds of creatures he was exposed to on these expeditions.

Robert Ripley had a keen interest in coral colony creatures and in 1932 acquired a giant Tridacna clam shell that he later used as a bird bath in his estate's garden.

In 1977 we published a paperback book that focused on many of the weirder, unbelievable undersea cartoons Ripley and his predecessors had published. This book, entitled ***Undersea Oddities,*** was one of our most successful books we have ever published, and was the inspiration for our new series of Marine Life books. ***Coral Colony Creatures*** is volume four in this series. It was felt that we needed to do another book similar in subject matter to "Oddities," but utilizing spectacular photos and the latest scientific data in addition to traditional Ripley cartoon drawings. The result is a book that we feel is the most colorful and exotic collection of creatures to be found anywhere, from tiny shrimp to giant squids, they are all here for your enjoyment.

Most of the creatures in this book are small and seldom seen in their natural environment. My personal favorite creatures are the stunningly beautiful sea slugs, or nudibranchs, a creature I have only personally seen once in the wild. Other people may be more interested in the creatures they have met on their dinner plates: lobsters, clams, shrimps and crabs. Others still I am sure will gravitate to the stars of many of the world's most famous aquariums, the octopuses, squids and nautiluses. Whatever your favorite sea creature may be, you will find some fun facts, unbelievable tales and scientific data on them within these pages.

Doug Perrine, the author of this book, is a world famous underwater photographer and author of several books— including ***Ripley's Whales & Dolphins.*** He is currently living in Hawaii where he dives as often as time allows. During his career he has dived at most of the world's great coral reefs and he has photographed everything from giant whales to minuscule mollusks. Many of his award-winning photographs have been used throughout this book to illustrate his insightful text.

Ripley's Coral Colony Creatures is an ambitious book. We have challenged the reader to examine some of the least glamorous of the ocean's creatures— worms, slugs, bivalve mollusks—and to see them in a different light, not just for themselves, but for the role they play in their environment. Every animal in the world has an important role in its ecosystem. The coral colonies of the world are truly one of the most bountiful and unique environments on our planet made all the more marvelous by their fascinating inhabitants. Enter this unusual realm and see for yourself, the colorful world of ***Ripley's Coral Colony Creatures.***

We hope you enjoy reading this book as much as we enjoyed writing and researching it.

Edward Meyer
Series Editor

Introduction

Ripley's cartoon for October 31st, 1941 featured Greta Smith of Oregon and her unusual pet octopus. Today, Pacific octopi are seldom kept as pets, but they are a favored attraction in aquariums all over the world.

When I was studying to be a Marine Biologist, I went to college at a University in Ohio far from the ocean. The Marine Laboratory at this school was very good and held many marine animals in dozens of marine aquariums using artificial seawater which, although common today, was somewhat experimental at the time. Although I entered my studies with a fascination for fish, it was in this marine lab that I gained an appreciation for the myriad of invertebrate species in the oceans.

As a part of the marine science curriculum at this school, we would spend our spring breaks at the beach every year, collecting animals for further study and to transport back to the lab in Ohio. We surveyed many different marine habitats in both Florida and Mississippi, ranging from wetlands and mudflats to open ocean surf beaches and barrier island lagoons. Much to my surprise at the time, the dominant animal groups we would find were not fish (even though there are an estimated 30,000 species), but rather we found mostly invertebrates (animals without backbones) of which there are millions of species! We found worms, and hydroids and anemones! We found clams and crabs and corals! We found shrimps and urchins and sea stars! We found squid and octopus and barnacles! We found sea squirts and mussels and sponges! I was amazed by the sheer variety of animals we were finding and how each species was uniquely adapted to its particular habitat. From the mole crab Emerita which battles the surf all day and night constantly re-burying itself in the sand in the surf zone, to the burrowing anemone. Cerianthus which could bury its beautiful body, tentacles and all, back into the mud faster than a camera flash. I was truly in awe of these animals' beauty and their ability to survive even the harshest living conditions.

In later years, in my career as an aquarist at public aquariums, I had the opportunity to care for a wider variety of invertebrates, and I was especially captivated by the cephalopods, such as the Giant Pacific Octopus. These species are incredibly intelligent for being relatively primitive animals and could actually learn to solve problems, such as the best way to get food out of a closed jar. Escaped octopuses always seem to know the direction of the adjacent open ocean too.

More recently, we have been able to explore the deep sea with unmanned "remotely-operated vehicles" or "ROVs." These robot submarines have shown us new species of invertebrates which are even more fascinating than their more common shallow water cousins.

As you read ***Ripley's Coral Colony Creatures*** *and experience the marine invertebrate world for yourself, you too will be as amazed as I was the first time I met these strange and wonderful creatures.*

Joseph M. Choromanski
Vice-President Husbandry
Ripley Aquariums, Inc.

Contents

Coral Colony Creatures

In 1992, Doctors at the University of South Florida Medical Center began using coral to replace human bone in reconstructive surgery.

Coral Reefs

When sailors from cold climates first entered tropical waters, they found an ocean very different from the one they knew back home. Their cold home waters were green, thick as soup with microorganisms, and teeming with fish. In the tropics, they found warm, blue water so clear that they could see through it for 100' (30 m) or more. Most of the time, as they gazed over the sides of their ships, however, they saw nothing but shafts of sunlight disappearing into the depths. Only when they reached shallow water did they start to see many fish, and structures unknown in colder waters: coral reefs.

Tropical waters are relatively void of life because they lack the chemical nutrients found in abundance in colder waters. These nutrients are the same ones found in a bag of garden fertilizer. Nitrogen and phosphorus are the most important. Adding these nutrients to a field makes crops grow. When they are present in seawater they nourish marine plants, called phytoplankton, turning the water green. These tiny plants feed tiny animals, which feed larger animals and so forth on up the food web. Where nutrient levels are low, the water is blue and clear because there are few of these tiny floating plants. Without the phytoplankton, there is no food to support the small creatures that form the food supply for larger fish. The surface waters of most tropical seas are like oceanic deserts. Unless there are currents called upwellings to bring nutrients up from the colder waters below, fish and other forms of life are normally scarce in the tropics.

There are, however, exceptions to this rule. Coral reefs abound with colorful fish and other organisms. They are like oases of life surrounded by watery blue deserts. According to scientific calculations, the level of nutrients in the surrounding water should not be able to support the amount of life found on coral reefs. How can so many different organisms exist in such a small space with so few nutrients?

Coral reefs are communities of interdependent organisms. The hard corals (pale), soft corals (red), and basslets (small orange fish) in this photo depend upon each other, and the other creatures of the reef, for various necessities of life.

Orange cup corals are non-reef-building corals. They have no zooxanthellae, and must nourish themselves entirely by capturing plankton.

The answer is recycling. Over millions of years of co-evolution, the plants and animals which live together on coral reefs have formed partnerships which enable them to pass nutrients back and forth so that the nutrients do not escape into the seawater to be carried away by currents. The wastes produced by one organism are the food for another and vice-versa. Often one organism becomes the food for another. In this way coral reefs are able to support a density of life which is among the highest of any ecosystem type on earth. In both total numbers of organisms and numbers of different types of organisms, coral reefs may equal or surpass tropical rain forests.

Corals themselves are organisms which may look like rocks, weeds, or flowers, but are actually animals that live together (in most cases) in colonies. Corals are dependent upon other organisms-which sometimes live within the tissues of the coral. A coral may be considered a community of organisms rather than an individual animal. The coral colony forms the foundation of a larger community-the reef, which is often likened by scientists to a city. The many different inhabitants of the reef community each have their own "job," or niche. By specializing in a particular lifestyle, the different types of organisms can each become very efficient in their own method of feeding and surviving, and the entire community can be more productive.

In this book, we will not have enough space to describe all of the millions of different organisms that live on coral reefs. We will leave the fish and other vertebrates (animals with backbones), for other books. We will look at the corals themselves, and some of the major groups of other invertebrates (animals without backbones) that live in and around the "cities" the corals build.

Not all corals live in colonies. This mushroom coral is a solitary coral, consisting of a single polyp.

Sea fans, sea plumes, sea whips, and other flexible corals belong to the group of corals known as gorgonians. When the polyps are extended, (as in this photo), it can be seen that each one has eight tentacles.

Castle-Building Corals

A coral's white skeleton shows through where the coral tissue has either died or "bleached" due to the loss of zooxanthellae. Bleaching occurs in response to environmental stress.

Corals form the construction crews that build most of the housing on the coral reef. Working together in colonies, they create massive formations out of their own limestone skeletons. Corals made the largest structure ever created by living things—the Great Barrier Reef of Australia. Corals cannot create such immense monuments by themselves, however. They need the help of microscopic plants called zooxanthellae (pronounced zoh-zan-THEL-ee) that live within their tissues.

These one-celled plants are able to perform a type of magic that animals cannot accomplish on their own. They use energy from the sun to convert water and carbon dioxide into molecules of food, by a process called photosynthesis. In this way they provide up to 98% of the food requirements of reef-building corals. The carbon dioxide they use is dissolved in seawater. Seawater also contains dissolved calcium, which corals are able to convert, through their own type of magic, into calcium carbonate, or limestone. Only corals with zooxanthellae are able to do this efficiently enough to build reefs.

The zooxanthellae produce food for the coral animals, while the corals protect them and fertilize them with their wastes. Most of the color in corals comes from the zooxanthellae. If a coral is stressed, for example by water that is too hot, it may lose its zooxanthellae and bleach white. If it is not able to regain zooxanthellae, it may die.

Not all corals require zooxanthellae, however. Non-reef-building corals get along just fine without them. While reef-building corals must live in shallow water (usually no deeper than 165' (50 m), in order for zooxanthellae to get enough light, non-reef-building corals can be found deeper than 330' (100 m). Nor do all corals produce hard skeletons. There are many types of soft corals, and some are very beautiful. Instead of external skeletons, like hard corals, soft corals have internal skeletons formed of protein and/or needle-like structures called spicules. The internal skeletons of soft corals are not solid, and allow the corals to change their shape and size by pumping water in and out.

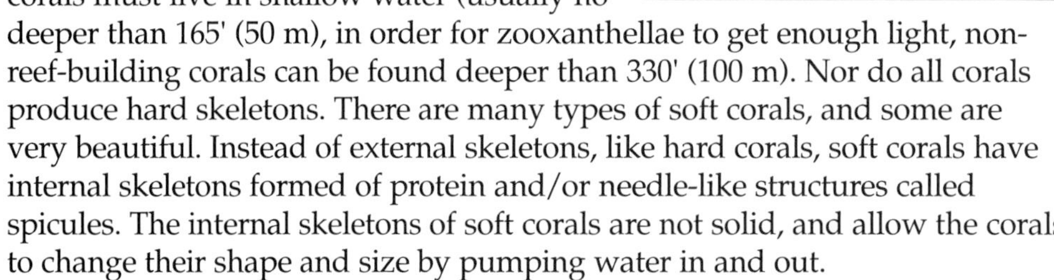

Where water quality is good, coral reefs can grow right up to the shoreline. Cutting down vegetation can cause siltation and runoff that inhibits the growth of corals.

Corals without zooxanthellae feed themselves by "hunting." Even those with zooxanthellae do some hunting to supplement their "farming." Usually they hunt at night. They capture food with a ring of tentacles around their mouths. The tentacles are armed with microscopic harpoon-like cells, called nematocysts, loaded with nerve poisons and activated by a hair trigger. When prey animals blunder against a tentacle, hundreds to thousands of these tiny toxic darts may be discharged at once. A soft-bodied animal such as a worm may be torn apart by the impact. The "harpoons" are useful for defense as well as capturing food. Fortunately, most are not capable of penetrating human skin. Some kinds, however, can produce a burning sensation and/or a rash—just one of several good reasons to avoid touching coral.

The darts paralyze the prey, so it can be pulled through the mouth into the gut, where it is digested. Any indigestible portions are expelled back out through the mouth. The simple body plan of corals only allows for a single opening.

By day the polyps of star corals are usually withdrawn inside their protective limestone cups.

At night the polyps of the star coral expand and extend their stinging tentacles to catch and feed upon plankton.

Corals are able to create large colonies by cloning themselves. A coral animal, called a polyp, can split in two, or it can produce a small bud, which develops into another polyp before splitting off. In this way a coral achieves something close to immortality. Individual polyps may die, but the colony lives on—sometimes for hundreds of years—long enough to produce massive coral heads weighing tons.

Cloning can allow a coral to produce copies of itself in one spot, but does not allow it to colonize new areas. To do this it has to produce a larva. A coral larva is called a planula, and looks like a tiny hairy sausage. It can swim, but generally drifts with the currents. Some corals can create planulae (plural of planula) without sexual reproduction but usually they are produced from the combination of eggs and sperm. In some cases, one coral produces sperm that is carried by currents to another coral and fertilizes its eggs. In others both eggs and sperm are released at the same time and find each other in the water to combine and produce planulae.

On some reefs many different types of coral release their eggs and sperm all at the same time on the same night producing an underwater blizzard that is one of the great spectacles of nature. Plankton-eating fish rush in to feast on all the eggs. So many eggs are produced that the fish cannot eat them all. Some survive to join the next generation of the reef construction crew.

The highest peaks of the Alps were built up by tiny sea shells! The Dolomites are "kalkalpen" or limestone mountains made up of tiny marine creature corpses.

The small pinkish particles floating upwards from this star coral colony are bundles of eggs and sperm, which are released only once per year. They will cross-fertilize with eggs and sperm from other colonies, which spawn at the same time on the same night.

In this close-up, some of the egg and sperm bundles are being released through the mouth of the coral polyps, while others are still "setting up" for release inside the polyp.

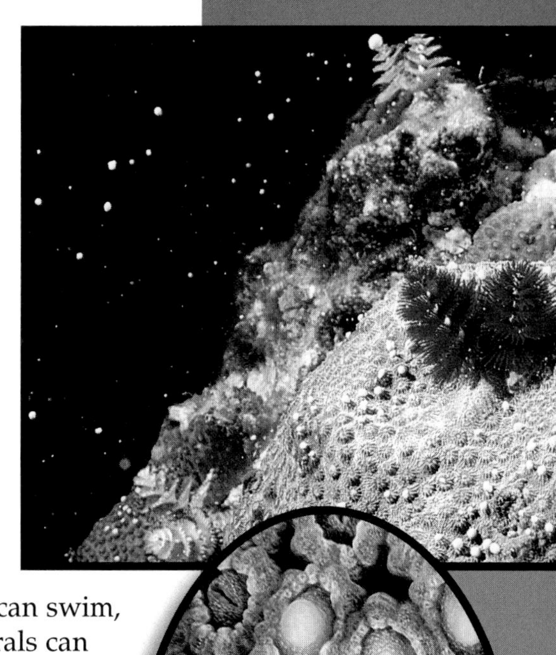

Colorful Coral Relatives

Like some anemones, false coral are capable of killing and devouring small fish. The deadly stinging cells are contained in the orange balls at the tips of the tentacles.

The feeding tentacles of a Portuguese man-of-war shown starting to digest a fish, are actually individual organisms which live with the other parts of the man-of-war as a colony or "super-organism."

Sea anemones get their name from the flowers called anemones, but unlike the flowers, their beauty hides a deadly predatory nature.

The Ocean Lights Luminous jellyfish sheds such brilliant light, that traveling in clusters, they light up the dark ocean for miles.

Corals are not the only sea creatures that use nematocysts to defend themselves and attack prey. A number of related animals employ the same type of weaponry in their underwater arsenals. What appears to us to be a realm of peace and tranquillity is actually a battleground where only the fittest survive. The stinging weapons employed by corals and their relatives are called "cnidae" from the Greek word for "nettle." Animals that have these stingers are called cnidarians. This group includes corals, sea anemones, sea jellies, and hydroids. The basic body plan of a cnidarian is a stomach opening to the outside through a mouth, with "fingers" (tentacles) around the mouth to pull in food. There are two main body forms: the polyp, and the medusa. A polyp is usually attached to the ocean bottom or another object, while a medusa usually floats free in the water. Some cnidarians, like corals, exist only as polyps, while others alternate between polyp and medusa during their life cycles.

Sea Anemones

Sea anemones are closely related to corals. An anemone can be thought of as a giant coral polyp, without the skeleton. Like corals, they exist only as polyps, never as medusae. Unlike corals, they are normally solitary and rarely found in groups. While some types of anemones build dwelling tubes, which function as a house or external skeleton, most do not. Some can actually walk around (very slowly) and at least one type is capable of swimming (very awkwardly).

Most anemones have some sort of shelter in the reef into which they can withdraw. However, they often lie out in the open, depending upon their stinging tentacles for protection. Often fish, crabs, or shrimp live within their tentacles. These small creatures have developed immunity to the anemone's sting. By hiding inside the anemone, they find safety from larger creatures, which are not immune to the stings. Some defend the anemone by biting or pinching anything that comes too close. They may also share food with the anemone, with one eating the scraps of the other's meals.

Some crabs take their relationship a step further by mounting the anemones onto their shells. They carry the anemone around as a "mobile defense system," which also helps to conceal and disguise the crab. Some crabs attach small anemones right to their claws to deliver a "knockout punch" when they get into a fight.

This sea anemone is shown in a partially contracted state, with [illegible]tacles [illegible]

Coral Relatives

The pink tips on the tentacles of this sea anemone may be warning colors, advertising the stinging cells which are used for both defense and feeding.

Sea anemones occur not only on tropical coral reefs, but in cooler waters as well. White plumose sea anemones are common along the Pacific northwest coast of North America.

A sea anemone consists of a single polyp. However, some sea anemones occur together in colonies.

Coral Relatives

"Strawberry anemones" are not true anemones, but colonial false corals, known to scientists as "corallimorphs."

Some anemones, like corals, have zooxanthellae, which help to feed them. Most, however, are dependent upon capturing animal food. With their larger size, and powerful stingers, some anemones are capable of capturing and devouring fish, crabs, shrimp, and other small animals, in addition to plankton. The stings of most sea anemones have little effect on humans, usually producing no more than a mild rash. However, a few kinds of anemones can produce a powerful reaction that has been compared to "sticking your finger in an electric socket." The most venomous types, can cause painful symptoms that last for weeks or months.

Like corals, anemones can reproduce sexually (by releasing sperm and eggs), or clone themselves by budding or dividing. Some "walking anemones" break off small pieces of their "foot" as they glide across the reef. These fragments may sprout tentacles and grow into whole new anemones. One writer compared this to "clipping a toenail and having it turn into a whole new you!"

Closely related to anemones, and corals, are animals known as zoanthids and corallimorphs, or "false corals." These creatures are very similar to anemones in appearance and lifestyle, but are often colonial, rather than solitary. They sometimes grow in such large colonies that they are referred to as "carpet anemones." Some types of zoanthid can be toxic. Hawaiian warriors used to rub them on the tips of their spears, in order to poison their enemies. The golden zoanthid forms a partnership with sponges. By growing in chains on the outer surface of the sponge, it gains a good perch from which to trap plankton for food. The sponge, in return, gains the chemical defenses of the zoanthid to protect it from sponge-eating angelfish, which are immune to the sponge's own chemical defenses.

The tentacles of sea anemones are like fingers. They sting the prey to disable or kill it, and then draw it into the mouth to be digested.

The bright colors of sea anemones may vary widely between different individuals. One anemone may be red, pink, or purple, while another of the same species may be white, green or cream-colored.

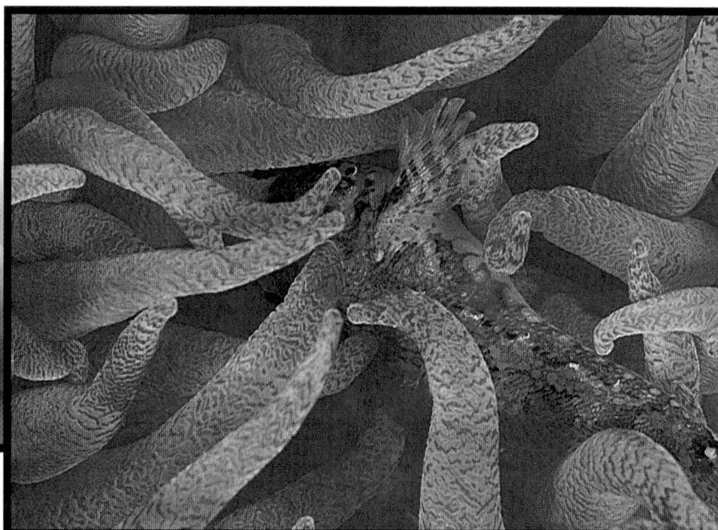

THE SEA ANEMONE IS CALLED THE FLOWER OF THE SEA--*YET IT PAINFULLY STINGS ITS PREY TO DEATH*

Sea Jellies

Some people refer to sea jellies as "jellyfish." They are not fish, however, but cnidarians. In sea jellies, the medusa, rather than the polyp, is the dominant form. Most sea jellies do pass through a polyp stage during the early part of their life cycle, but this form is small and inconspicuous. The medusa stage can also be very small. In some jellies it is barely visible to the naked eye. In others, such as the lion's mane jellyfish, the medusa can grow over 6' 6" (2 m) across, with tentacles 132' (40 m) long, and weigh over a ton. More than 99% of that weight may be water.

Most sea jellies have stingers on their tentacles, which they use both for defense and catching food. Trailing their tentacles like fishing lines, some can catch fish larger than themselves, paralyzing them with powerful toxins. Some kinds of box jellies, cousins to the true sea jellies, are so venomous that a tentacle across the chest, near the heart, can kill a swimmer instantly. Box jellies, or sea wasps, are square, rather then round, with four tentacles, and should always be avoided. Some beaches in Australia are closed to swimming all summer long because of the danger of box jellies.

Some jellies are accompanied by small fish that have developed immunity to their stingers, and use them as a shelter from larger predators. Small crabs, lobsters and other animals have been known to ride on the bell of a sea jelly, and even steer it to place it between themselves and some threat. Some crabs capture sea jellies and attach them to their backs for protection. Some fish, like the African pompano, when they are small, grow thread-like extensions to their fins, that can be several times as long as the fish's own body. Some scientists believe that this makes the fish look like a sea jelly, and frightens predators away.

Coral Relatives

Not all sea jellies have stingers. These jellies do not need stingers for feeding because they are able to "farm" algae within their bodies.

The giant purple jellyfish (Cyanea Arctica) has 8 eyes and 8 ears.

Many sea jellies have a reproductive stage attached to the bottom. Each tier of this reproductive "umbrella" will break off one at a time to form a separate free-floating medusa.

THE GIANT JELLYFISH (Cyanea Arctica) MEASURES 7 FEET ACROSS AND HAS TENTACLES 140 FEET LONG

Hydromedusas are usually small and transparent. This one has red eye spots, which can sense light and dark, at the bases of the tentacles.

Sea jellies can grow much larger than hydromedusas—often larger than a human.

The head of a sun jellyfish can grow to be 8 feet across and its tentacles can measure 200 feet in length.

You might imagine that nothing in its right mind would eat an animal that is mostly water and loaded with deadly stingers. Fish, crabs, sea turtles, and even humans, however, are known to eat sea jellies. Some turtles eat so many sea jellies that it has been suggested that they get "high" from the nerve poisons in the stingers. Leatherback sea turtles subsist on a diet that consists almost exclusively of sea jellies. In laboratory tests, sea jellies were shown to contain almost no food energy at all, so it is hard to explain how a turtle could survive on this diet, but leatherbacks grow rapidly on it, achieving weights of over 990 lbs. (450 kg) In Asia, sea jellies are dried and eaten as snacks and used as ingredients in traditional medicines.

A tangle of sea jelly or hydromedusa tentacles acts much like a fishing net—a net that kills on contact.

Like corals and anemones, some kinds of sea jellies contain zooxanthellae that produce food by photosynthesis. "Upside-down jellyfish" spend most of their time lying on their backs on the seafloor, basking in the sun so that their zooxanthellae can produce enough food for them. In some saltwater lakes on tropical islands there are stingless sea jellies which follow the sun from one side of the lake to the other. Since they produce all the food they need by "farming," and no predators are present in their small lakes, they have no need for stingers.

Most sea jellies get around by jet propulsion, contracting their bodies to force out water. Although they may seem to be wandering aimlessly, they are capable of swimming with a purpose, directed by up to 16 sets ofsensory organs. These include primitive "eyes" that sense light and dark, and "ears" that give them a sense of balance. Box jellies have complex eyes with a lens and retina. Some jellies can not only detect light, but actually produce it. One kind of "glow-in-the-dark" sea jelly has a scientific name that means "night light" (noctiluca).

Moon jellyfish have four stomachs visible near the center of the dome, and sometimes occur in dense swarms. Swimmers may experience a mild stinging sensation if they contact this species.

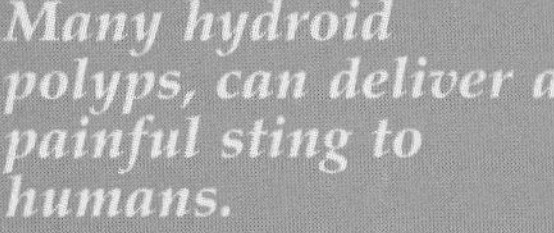
Many hydroid polyps, can deliver a painful sting to humans.

HYDROIDS

Hydroids are less familiar than corals and sea jellies, but people who fail to recognize them sometimes get a very painful education! Hydroids are usually small, and often encrust other organisms or structures. They may appear as feather-like or weed-like growths on reefs, or pier pilings. With some hydroids, the polyp is the dominant form; in others, the medusa is dominant; and some alternate between medusa and polyp during their life cycle. Hydromedusas are similar in appearance to sea jellies, but slightly different in structure, and do not grow as large.

Some hydroids exist as solitary polyps, but many are colonial. Unlike coral colonies, where each individual is identical to all the others, in hydroid colonies there are always at least two different polyp forms, and sometimes a number of specialized forms. Sometimes medusas and several kinds of polyps all live together in a colony, each performing a specialized function. In this way, hydroid colonies are similar to colonies of ants and other social insects. Some hydroid colonies (such as the Portuguese man-of-war) function like a fishing village with different individuals all plying their own trades. Some polyps do the fishing; others work as soldiers to defend the colony. Some do the eating and digesting; others are responsible for reproduction; and still others for locomotion (using jet propulsion). A modified medusa forms a float that keeps the colony from sinking.

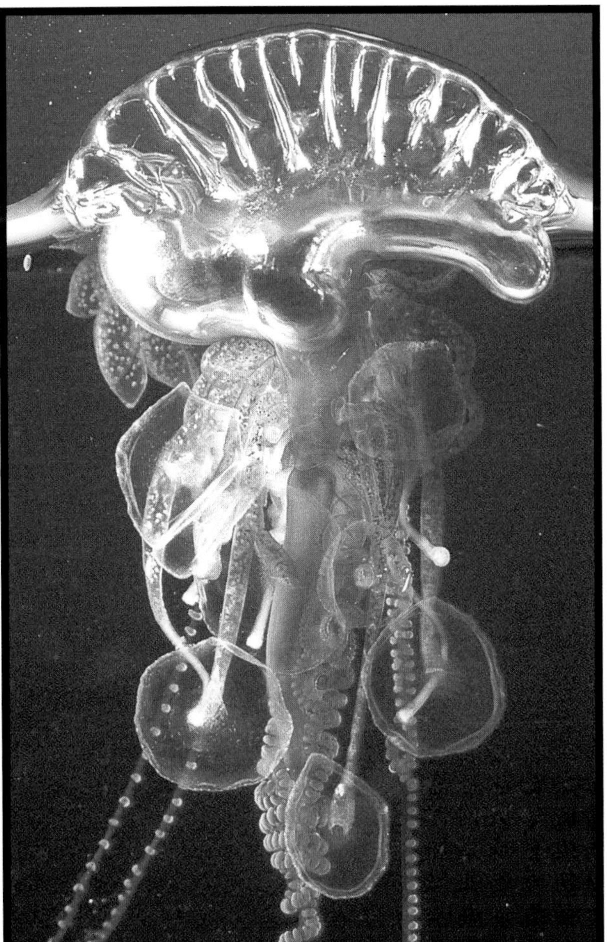

The Portuguese man-of-war is a colonial hydroid, consisting of numerous specialized individuals. It floats on the surface with its tentacles trailing underwater.

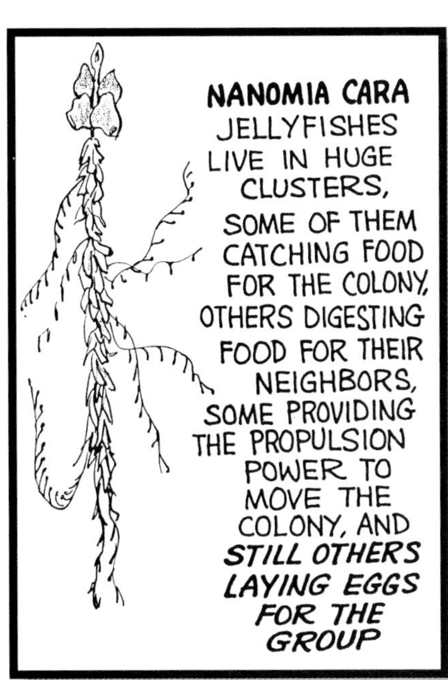

A close view of the tentacles of a Portuguese man-of-war shows stinging cells, which have been discharged. Each barbed harpoon is connected to a sac of venom.

The man-of-war and some of its relatives, such as the by-the-wind-sailor, use wind power to move around the ocean and troll for fish. They can sail at a 45-degree angle to the wind using their floats as sails. Some are "left handed" and some are "right handed," so they move in different directions when the wind blows. The floats are not filled with air, but with carbon monoxide—a poisonous gas to which they are immune. The stinging tentacles dangle as far as 33' (10 m) below the rest of the colony. The sting from a man-of-war can kill an adult human, but usually only causes a painful injury. The stinging cells can remain active long after the rest of the colony has died or been broken apart. For this reason it is wise to be careful when walking near the high-tide line where floating debris has been deposited on a beach.

Some hydroids contain zooxanthellae or other algae that help to nourish them, but most gather food with their stinging cells. Some organisms, such as the man-of-war fish, have developed immunity to the stingers and hide among them for protection. One type of open-ocean octopus is known to grab pieces of man-of-war tentacles and use them for defense. Some sea slugs actually eat hydroids without discharging the stinging cells. Then they move the cells into their own defensive organs and use the stingers for self-defense. Some sea slugs can eat hydroids that contain zooxanthellae without harming the zooxanthellae. They then farm the zooxanthellae within their own bodies.

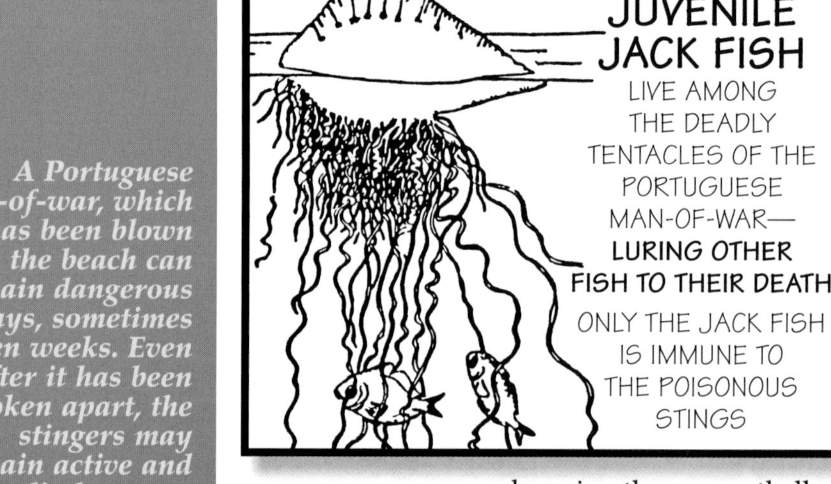

A Portuguese man-of-war, which has been blown onto the beach can remain dangerous for days, sometimes even weeks. Even after it has been broken apart, the stingers may remain active and discharge on contact with bare skin.

Some types of colonial hydroids build limestone skeletons. These are known as fire corals, because of the sensation that comes from touching them. The first treatment for an injury from any cnidarian should be to remove any tentacles or other parts that are still clinging to the skin. This must be done carefully to avoid discharging more stingers. Shaving cream and a razor are said to be effective for removing some types of tentacles. Washing in cold salt water may also help, but NEVER apply fresh water, which will cause more stingers to fire. Vinegar and ice packs (NOT ice water) can also be helpful. If these are not available, a gentle application of meat tenderizer, baking soda, or rubbing alcohol can sometimes help. After all traces of the stinging tentacles have been removed, hydrocortisone cream can be applied. If the injury is serious, expert medical help should be sought immediately.

A comb jelly feeds by means of long, sticky tentacles. Small lures on the tentacles resemble plankton, and attract prey.

Comb Jellies

There are some coral relatives that do not have stinging cells. Instead, they have sticky cells. They catch food by the "flypaper method," rather than the harpoon method. Scientists call these animals ctenophores (TEE-no-fores), but they are commonly known as "comb jellies." They have hair-like structures called cilia arranged in rows like the teeth of a comb. The cilia move in a wave-like motion to propel the animal, or to direct food toward its mouth. The cilia are usually so close together that they can split light like a prism, producing a shimmering rainbow effect, with waves of color rippling down the sides of the animal. Most ctenophores also glow green in the dark.

Most comb jellies are planktonic and transparent, and easily confused with sea jellies. A variety of interesting forms have common names such as "sea walnut," "sea gooseberry," and "Venus' girdle." A few unusual comb jellies have adapted to life on the ocean bottom, and look like flatworms. Some spend their lives attached to sea stars, sea urchins, or other animals. They feed by means of long sticky threads that wave about in the current, sticking to small food particles.

The comb rows of a comb jelly are visible in this close up. Inside the comb jelly is a krill (small shrimp-like organism), with two dark eyes, which is being digested.

The castle of Orford in England constructed in 1165 has walls consisting of fossilized jellyfish.

Hair-like cilia on a comb jelly are so close together that they split light rays into different colors to create "rainbows" which travel up and down the comb rows.

Spectacular Sponges

The sponge at the bottom is releasing small orange eggs. They will be fertilized by sperm released by another sponge on another part of the reef.

A sponge must filter one ton of water to get enough food to gain one ounce of body weight.

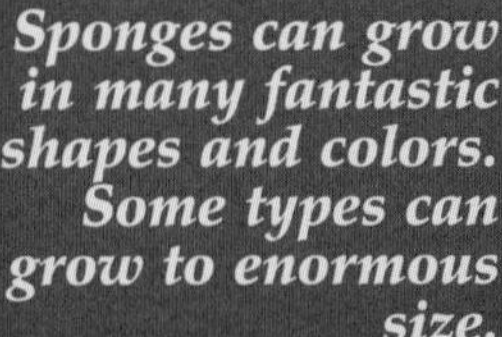

Sponges are among the simplest of all multi-cellular animals. They have no specialized tissues or organs: no brain or nerves; no muscles; no mouth or stomach; no reproductive organs; no eyes or, ears. Yet, they are able to feed, defend themselves, and reproduce so well that they are among the most common organisms on coral reefs, and sometimes the largest. Some types reach sizes of up to 10' (3 m). They are often very beautiful as well.

Adult sponges are always attached to the ocean bottom or some other object. Most are unable to move, but some types can creep around very slowly like an amoeba. They feed by filtering particles out of the water. Sponges have been called the air-conditioning system of the undersea city. A sponge weighing only $2\frac{1}{4}$ lb. (1 kg) can filter 6,240 gallons (24,000 liters) of water per day! Sponges can filter out up to 96% of the bacteria in seawater. Water is pumped in through numerous small holes on the outside of the sponge, and pumped out through one or more larger holes. Food particles are trapped on the way through and either digested by the cell which traps them, or shared with other cells. In this way, all cells of the sponge are nourished, and the water flowing over the coral reef becomes clearer. Some sponges have small algae similar to zooxanthellae living inside them that help to nourish them. Other sponges, including toxic fire sponges, live on the roots of mangroves—shoreline trees that dangle their roots into the ocean—and exchange nutrients with the tree. The cladorhizids, a type of deep-water sponge, have recently been discovered to trap and feed on small shrimp.

Most sponges, however, are no threat to any animal large enough to be seen with the naked eye. In fact, they often serve as homes for up to thousands of other animals, from shrimp and crabs to sea stars and sea cucumbers. They provide shelter, and create water currents that assist the other animals. Some crabs trim off pieces of sponge to fit their shells, and attach them to disguise themselves. The pieces of sponge continue to live and grow.

Sponges can grow in many fantastic shapes and colors. Some types can grow to enormous size.

Like corals, sponges use water currents to reproduce. Male sponges sometimes release such thick clouds of sperm that they appear to be smoking. Female sponges may release eggs at the same time, or they may draw the sperm into their own tissues and fertilize eggs within their own bodies. Some sponges are both male and female, and some change from one sex to the other.

Sponges play an important role in controlling water and in the competition for space and nutrients in the reef ecosystem.

Some sponges are shaped like urns or barrels, with the water flowing in through the outer surface, and leaving the sponge through the center. Other sponges are shaped like tubes, fingers, antlers, elephant ears, knobs, blobs, or like a thin crust on top of something else. The body is supported by protein fibers and/or spicules of limestone or silica. Most sponges are soft, but in some of the limestone sponges, the spicules fuse into a solid rock-like mass. In some of the silica sponges, or glass sponges, the spicules fuse together to form intricate, lacy skeletons, which are prized in Japan because of their delicate beauty. The "Venus' flower basket" glass sponge usually contains a pair of shrimp, which are trapped within the sponge and mated for life. In one type of sponge, the *Rosella* sponge, the glass-like silica spicules appear to work like fiber optic cables to transmit light inside the sponge's body to promote the growth of algae, which produce food for the sponge.

A sponge cut into numerous pieces can regenerate itself to become a whole organism.

VENUS' FLOWER BASKET
a deep-sea sponge
IS A POPULAR JAPANESE WEDDING PRESENT BECAUSE IT ALWAYS SHELTERS 2 CRUSTACEANS - *WHICH TO THE JAPANESE ARE SYMBOLS OF GOOD LUCK*

The spicules form an important part of the sponge's defensive system. These needle-like structures can penetrate the skin of an animal or person that touches the sponge-producing an irritation similar to that caused by fiberglass. Additionally, many sponges produce toxic or noxious chemicals. Some sponges use chemicals to create a "dead zone" around them so that other organisms will not crowd them. Certain sponges are carefully avoided by divers because of the unpleasant sensation that results from touching them. These go by names such as "fire sponge" and "dread red sponge." The bright colors of many sponges may be advertisements for their unpleasant qualities. Most sea creatures will not feed on sponges. Exceptions include hawksbill sea turtles, angelfish, and nudibranchs (sea slugs). Recently scientists have become very interested in using chemical compounds from sponges to treat cancer and other diseases.

Sponges have amazing abilities to repair themselves, and can often recover completely if even a small part of the sponge is left intact. Some sponges can be pureed in a blender and strained through a cheesecloth to separate the cells, and will re-organize themselves to form a new sponge! If a sponge is injured, it does not have to grow new cells to repair the wound, as any other animal would—it can merely move existing cells around to "plug the hole." Some sponges can also change their shape as needed, for example spreading themselves out to take over some neighboring territory on the reef that has become vacant. This amazing flexibility is one of the reasons that these primitive animals have been so successful.

Sponges provide habitat for many small organisms such as transparent shrimp.

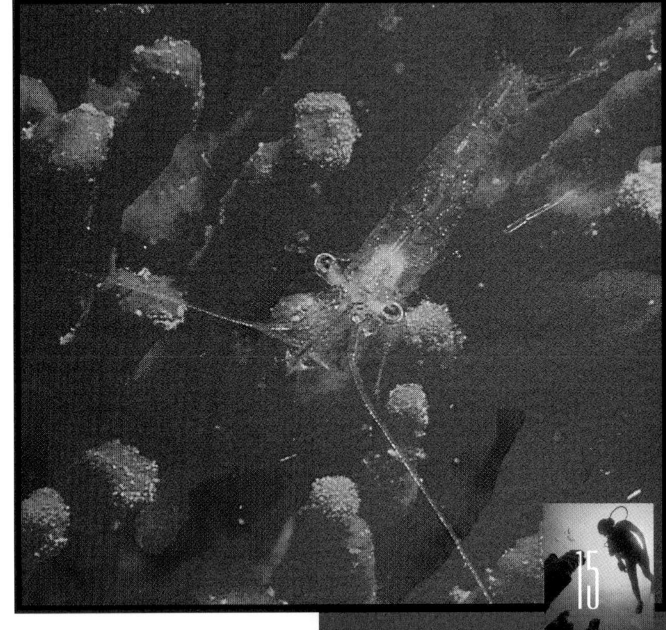

Squishy Sea Squirts

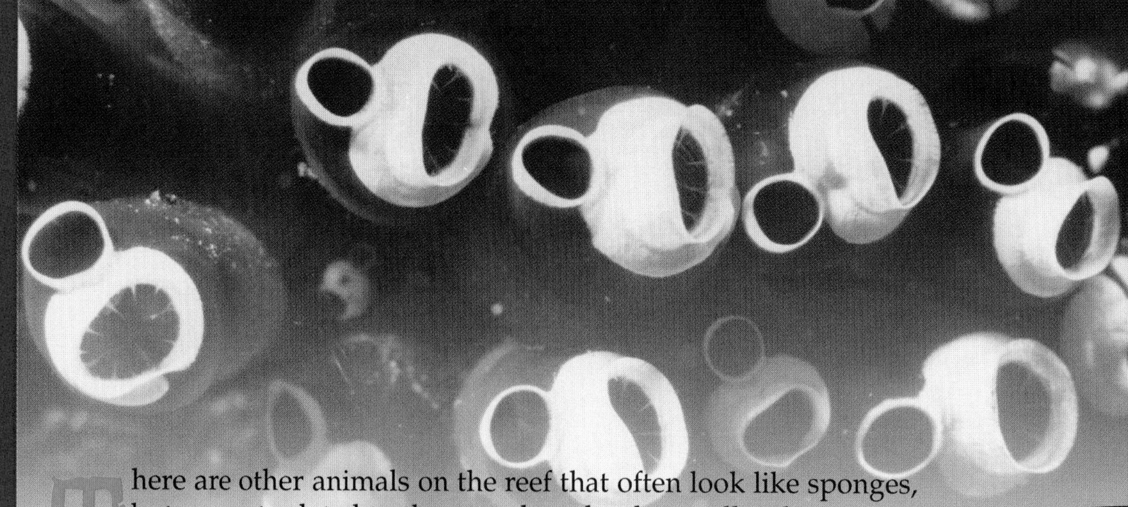

Sea Squirts usually have two large openings for water circulation. The filter baskets can be seen inside the siphons (openings) of these colonial sea squirts.

There are other animals on the reef that often look like sponges, but are not related to them, and tend to be smaller than sponges. These are commonly known as "sea squirts" because, when they are found out of the water at low tide, touching one will sometimes cause it to squirt out a jet of water. Scientists refer to this group of animals as tunicates, because the internal organs are enclosed by a cloak-like layer, or "tunic."

Most tunicates feed in a manner similar to sponges, except that instead of drawing water in through many small openings, they draw water in through one large opening, filter out food particles through a basket-like structure inside, and pump the water out through another large opening. The presence of two major openings, of about the same size, is a good clue that you are looking at a sea squirt, rather than a sponge.

While tunicates may appear to be very simple animals, they are considered to be among the most evolutionarily advanced of the invertebrates. This analysis is based not on the adult form, but on the larval stages. While the adults sit attached to the reef, pumping water and sifting plankton, the larvae swim around in the plankton almost like small fishes. They are called tadpole larvae. These larvae do not have backbones, but they do have a nerve cord that corresponds to our spinal cord, and a stiff tissue rod, which strengthens it like a backbone. Some scientists consider sea squirts to be our closest relatives among the invertebrates. They share a similar life progression, with the youngsters roaming wild and free, and the adults settling down to a life of hard work so that they can reproduce.

(right) Tunicates come in a variety of colors including blue, green and yellow.

(left) Tunicates occur in cold seas, as well as tropical waters. These "light bulb tunicates" are found off the southern coast of Australia.

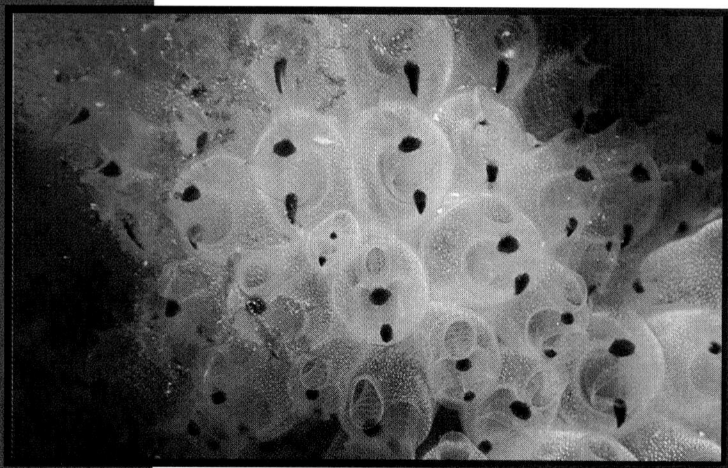

Sea Squirts

Nudibranchs or sea slugs (at right) often live in tandem with sea squirts on a tropical reef.

There are several different kinds of tunicates. The largest group is the ascidians, which live attached to the ocean bottom or other objects. Some live alone, while others grow in colonies. Although they resemble sponges, and obtain their food in the same way, their bodies are much more complex than those of sponges. Tunicates have a heart, a stomach, an intestine, nerves and a "brain," muscles, gills, blood vessels, reproductive organs, etc. Their hearts are unusual in that they reverse the direction of pumping every two to three minutes. Their blood is even more unusual. Special blood cells may be loaded with strong acids, or with iron or vanadium, a rare metal which sometimes reaches a concentration more than 10 million times that of seawater! Most ascidians are filter feeders, but a few deep-sea forms are able to capture small animals.

These creeping tunicates are digesting food. Water enters the intake siphon, and passes out through the exit siphon. On the way through, food particles are trapped in the filter basket.

Another kind of tunicates are the salps. They live in colonies in the open ocean, floating in the plankton, and swimming by jet propulsion. They are usually transparent like sea jellies, but are usually shaped either like long tubes or like chains of little jet engines, joined side to side. Many produce light in the same way as a chemical light stick, and they can be just as bright. Some salps form cylinders up to 33' (10 m) long and wide enough for a diver to swim right through the middle of them. Some salps can grow 10% of their body length per hour. For a person 5' (1.5 m) tall, this would be like adding another 6" (15 cm) in height every hour!

Some sea squirts can be as delicate and beautiful as blown glass. These tunicates are less than an inch long.

Another kind of tunicates are the larvaceans, because they resemble the larvae of other tunicates. The sponge-like adult stage is never reached. Instead the larvacean looks like a tadpole for its entire life. It still manages to filter feed, though, by using a mucus net within a jelly-like "house" that it secretes for itself. It floats around in the plankton, using its tail to drive water through the "house," trapping food in the filters. As might be expected of an animal that never grows up, the larvacean never cleans its house, but just moves out when it gets dirty, and builds a new one.

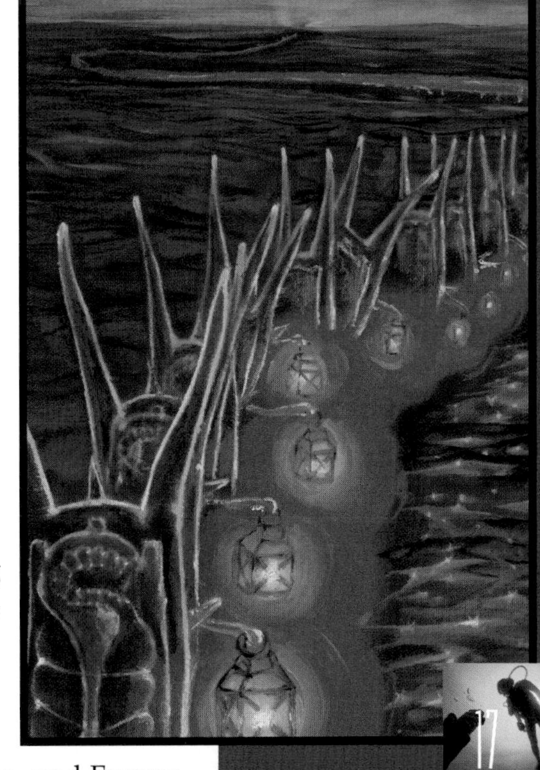

Salps are tinted with red phosphorescence and are attached to their relatives by a transparent thread. Family chains may reach 40 miles long and in olden times were mistaken by sailors for sea serpents.

Tunicates can clone themselves by budding, or they can reproduce sexually. Most are both male and female at the same time. Some release their eggs and sperm into the water through an opening at the end of their bodies. In some colonial species, though, the body wall may rupture to permit the release of sperm, eggs, or larvae.

Certain kinds of large sea squirts are considered delicacies in some countries. Large quantities are eaten by epople in Chile, Korea, Japan, and Europe.

Wonderful Wiggly Worms

The bright colors of the zebra flatworm may be a warning of toxic defensive chemicals inside.

Worms get little respect, but they play important roles in the ocean ecosystem and some rank among the most attractive members of the reef community. There are at least 17 major groups of marine animals that we call "worms." Most are not closely related to each other. Flatworms are among the most primitive of all animals. Acorn worms are considered to be more advanced than squid or crabs, and are related to animals with backbones. These 17 groups include tens of thousands of different species.

The simple flatworms may have been the ancestors of mollusks and crustaceans. They have no blood systems and no gills, but breathe right through their skin! They are soft and thin. They feed on other animals, including each other. Some kinds subdue their prey with sticky glue that they make. One kind inserts a straw-like apparatus into sea squirts, dissolves them with digestive fluids, and then sucks them up like someone sipping soda through a straw. Others simply swallow their prey. Many live inside their victims as parasites. Some kinds glide around the reef like miniature flying carpets. Some flatworms are brightly colored, and very beautiful. In nature, bright colors are often used as a warning sign, meaning that the animal is so dangerous it does not have to hide. The most colorful flatworms probably contain toxic chemicals.

Flatworms have an amazing ability to repair their bodies. Some kinds can grow a new head if their existing one is cut off. If one is cut in two, it will become two flatworms. They can reproduce by splitting apart, by budding, or by sexual reproduction. Most are both male and female at the same time.

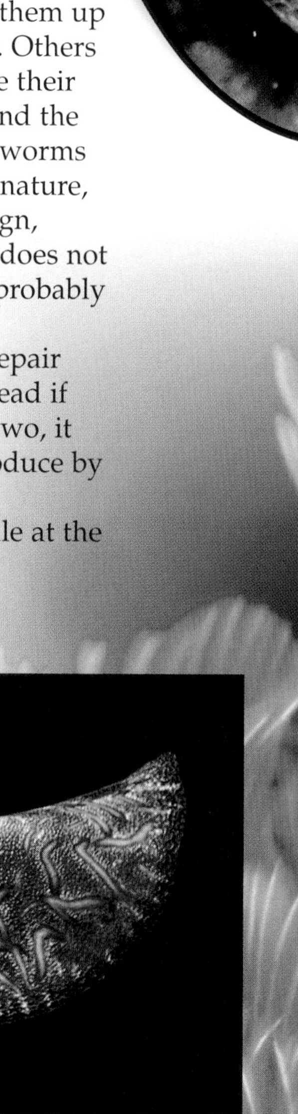

While flatworms are usually seen gliding across the reef, they are also capable of swimming by undulating their bodies with a graceful rippling motion

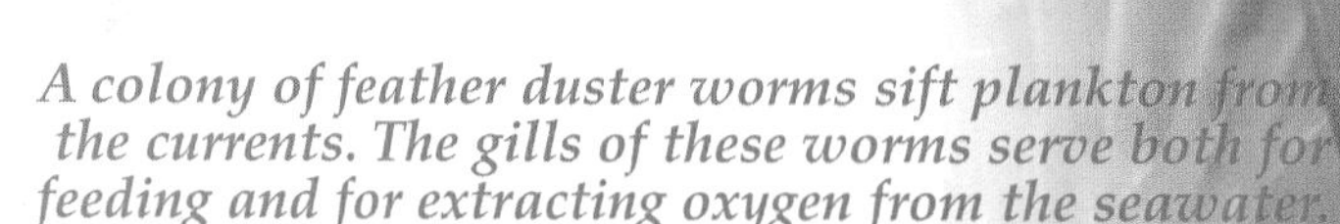

A colony of feather duster worms sift plankton from the currents. The gills of these worms serve both for feeding and for extracting oxygen from the seawater.

Ribbon worms are considered more advanced than flatworms. They can also grow much larger. One kind can reach nearly 198' (60 m) in length. That is twice as long as a blue whale! They hunt with a spear-like "tongue" which they thrust out of a hole in the tip of their heads and which may be armed with nerve poison. In some types, the "tongue" is used like a whip, which wraps around the prey.

Some ribbon worms can reproduce by splitting apart, but most reproduce by casting eggs and sperm into the water. Each individual is either male or female, but some may change their sex from male to female.

Segmented worms are even more advanced. Their bodies are made of identical segments, like Leggo toys. Each section has muscles, nerves and blood vessels that join to the same part in the next section. They are very common, both on reefs and in the plankton. This group includes the beautiful feather duster worms and Christmas tree worms that live inside tubes. The only part of tube worms we can see is the colorful gills, which are used for both breathing and feeding. They feed by straining small particles of plankton from the water.

Living near deep-sea volcanic vents, thousands of meters down in the ocean, there are giant tube worms that can grow more than 10' (3 m) long. These worms have no mouth or stomach. They live entirely off food that is produced for them by bacteria that live inside their bodies. The relationship is similar to the relationship between corals and zooxanthellae. The bacteria, however, are not able to accomplish photosynthesis in the darkness of the deep sea. Instead they obtain energy from poisonous sulfur gasses that are emitted from the volcanic vents. The worms collect the sulfur gas and supply it to the bacteria, along with oxygen. These worms survive in water as hot as 482° farenheit (250 degrees C)!

Ribbon worms, are rarely seen by divers because they usually hide under ledges or inside coral heads or rubble. Unlike tube worms, they are active hunters.

Christmas tree worms, come in as many colors as Christmas tree ornaments. They use their gills to filter plankton.

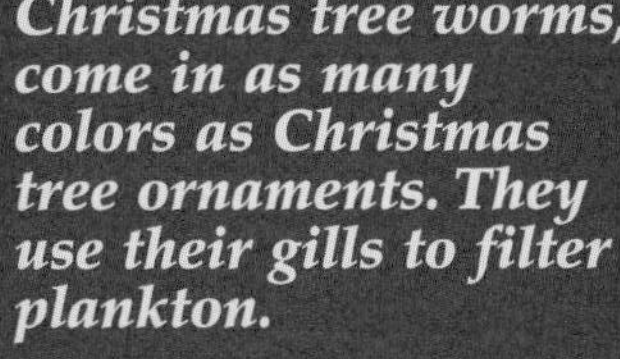

Worms

A spaghetti worm's sticky tentacles will adhere food particles, then draw them back to the mouth of the worm, which remains safely hidden inside its hole on the reef.

Spaghetti worms stretch their long sticky feeding tentacles out along the ocean bottom, and wait for particles of food to stick to them. Then they pull their tentacles back into their tube, wipe off the food, and stretch their tentacles back out again. Other segmented worms are active predators. The "bobbit worm" flips its jaws out of its head to seize its victim, then pumps poison into it. This worm is able to draw dissolved metals out of seawater and store them in its jaws, making them very hard. Some types of bobbit worms can grow 6' 6" –9' 9" (2 – 3 m) long and as big around as a man's arm. These large worms can attack large prey, such as fish and octopus.

Bobbit worms are less of a threat to divers than much smaller segmented worms called bristle worms or fire worms. These harmless-looking worms carry bundles of tiny bristles that have been compared to hollow glass tubes filled with venom. If the worm is touched, the bristles will pierce the skin of the aggressor and break off. The venom produces a burning sensation that is not soon forgotten.

Most segmented worms reproduce through production of eggs and sperm, but some do it in odd ways. In some segmented worms (mostly tube-dwellers), the part of the worm containing the reproductive organs breaks off and swims to the surface to reproduce with other segments, leaving the rest of the worm safe inside its tube. In certain species, the reproductive segments glow in the dark, making it easier for them to find each other. In some South Pacific islands, these reproductive parts of sea worms are eaten as a delicacy.

Bristle worms, or fire worms, are small, but pose a hazard to divers. The white bristles are brittle and hollow, and contain venom. If touched, the bristles penetrate and break off, producing an irritation similar to "fiberglass rash."

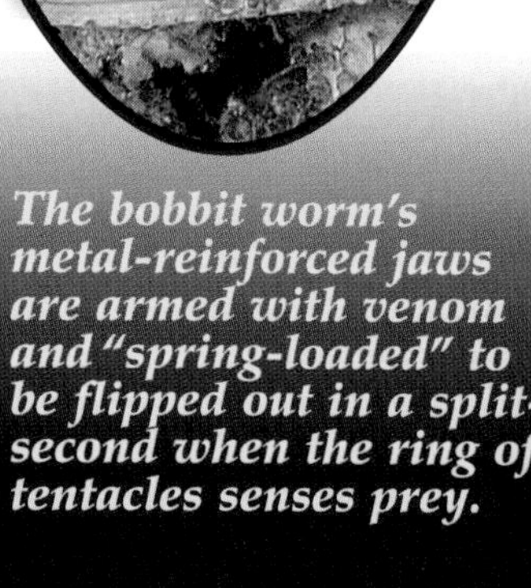

The bobbit worm's metal-reinforced jaws are armed with venom and "spring-loaded" to be flipped out in a split-second when the ring of tentacles senses prey.

The delicate gill whorls of Christmas tree worms are equipped with eye spots that can detect the shadow of an approaching predator. Either a sudden change in light level or a slight water movement will cause the worm to retract the gills instantly into its tube.

Crusty Crustaceans

The giant hermit crab of Alaska carries a mollusk shell for protection. When it withdraws inside the shell, one claw can be placed across the opening to seal it and prevent a predator from gaining access.

The segmented worms were probably the ancestors of another group of segmented animals, which contains at least 75% of the animals on earth. These are the joint-legged animals including insects, spiders, and a large class of marine animals called crustaceans. This class includes crabs, lobsters, shrimps, barnacles and their relatives. Joint-legged animals have antennae, but only the crustaceans have two pairs. The joint-legged animals all have skeletons, sometimes called shells, which are born on the outside of the body, like a crust. The skeletons of crustaceans and their allies do not grow with their bodies, as ours do. Instead, crustaceans must shed their shells from time to time and make larger ones. Crustacean shells are not made of heavy limestone, like those of molluscs and corals, but of a lighter material called chitin (KITE-in). The lighter shells enable them to be more active, but are also more easily broken by predators. Chitin from crab shells is used for a variety of products, including surgical sutures, food, drugs, cosmetics, clothes, and water filters.

In 17th century America, pigs were fed shellfish, including crabmeat and lobsters, because it was considered unfit for human consumption.

Spiny lobsters do not have large claws like Maine lobsters. They use their spiny antennae as defensive weapons, as well as sensory organs, and feed with a variety of appendages, including their walking legs.

The candy stripe shrimp gains shelter and protection by living on a crimson sea anemone.

This rock crab's pinch is not painful enough to deter the sculpin from attacking it. The crab is safe only as long as it maintains its grip on the fish. When it lets go, the fish may swallow it.

A railway train was stalled by thousands of crabs, which made the rails so slippery the train was unable to move. Manzanillo, Mexico (1950s).

CRABBY CRABS

Crabs have five pairs of legs. The forward pair is usually enlarged into claws. When they are disturbed, crabs raise their claws and try to pinch whatever is bothering them. Sometimes a crab will pinch onto an animal (or person) that is attacking it, then cast off its claw and run away. The claw continues to pinch the attacker while the crab escapes. The crab can seal the wound without bleeding and grow a new claw to replace the one that has been lost.

Crabs do not use their claws only for defense. They are also used for feeding and other jobs. The large coconut crabs of the South Pacific are said to be capable of opening coconuts with their claws. The claws of some crabs have large "teeth" on them, and can crush a clam, or break a human finger.

Crabs also use their claws for communication. Fiddler crabs use their claws like semaphore flags to signal each other. Different colonies of fiddler crabs even have different "languages." Stone crabs also "talk" to each other with their claws, but they live in muddy water where they cannot see each other. So instead of waving their claws to signal each other, they make noises with them. Each claw has a pattern like a fingerprint on it. The crab uses one claw to scrape this area on the other claw, making a noise that other crabs can hear.

The male fiddler crab has one greatly enlarged claw. The claw is used primarily as a signaling device to attract females and threaten other males.

The Coconut crab of the Indian and Pacific oceans, which is 2 feet long and weighs 6 pounds, climbs trees, hurls coconuts to the ground and can open cracked ones with its powerful claws.

A decorator crab adorns its body with sponges and hydroids. These serve not only to conceal and disguise the crab, but also lend the protection of their toxic chemicals and stinging cells.

Hermit crabs do not rely on the protection of their own shells and claws. Instead, they crawl into the abandoned shells of sea snails, and carry them around like a mobile home. The crab's body grows twisted to better fit into the shell. As the crab grows, it must move into a larger shell from time to time. It is not unusual to see two hermit crabs fighting over a nice shell.

The giant Japanese spider crab can develop a leg span of up to 12 feet. These crabs are highly valued for food in Japan.

Some hermit crabs increase their protection by attaching sea anemones to their mobile home. The stinging tentacles of the anemone discourage predators, and help to hide the crab as well. Some crabs just attach the anemones directly to their claws, like brass knuckles. Other crabs cover their shells with all sorts of material for camouflage, including live corals, hydroids, and sponges. It is often impossible to detect the crab unless it moves.

One kind of Japanese crab grows more than 12' across.

Some crabs swim in the open ocean. Usually these crabs are quite small. They can occur in large swarms, and are an important food source for other animals. Crabs that live on the bottom, in the deep sea, can grow much larger.

THE CRAB THAT THROWS "GRENADES"

The mellia tessellata A CRAB FOUND IN THE INDIAN OCEAN, DEFENDS ITSELF BY GRASPING AND SHAKING SEA ANEMONES—WHICH CAN DELIVER A PAINFUL STING—AT ITS ADVERSARIES

All Japanese Heike Gani crabs appear to have a face on their backs, but it is very rare to find a common Blue crab with a face on its carapace!

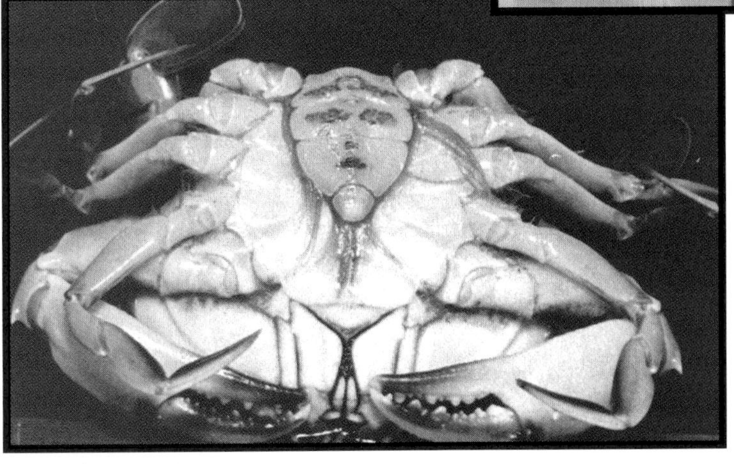

Heike Gani crabs found off the Japanese Island of Shikoku, appear to have the face of a samurai warrior on their shells, and are believed to be the spirits of soldiers who died in The Battle of Dun No Ura in 1185.

The porcelain crab is immune to the stinging tentacles of the anemone in which it resides.

In May 1881, a rain of crabs fell over Worcester, England!

Some crabs live with other organisms. Sea cucumber crabs live inside the mouth of a sea cucumber. Coral guard crabs live within the branches of corals. They defend the coral from sea stars and other predators that might attack it. They will even rush out and pinch a crown-of-thorns starfish that approaches the coral. The coral repays the crab with both shelter, and food from its zooxanthellae. The food is concentrated in the tips of the coral polyp's tentacles. The crab snips them off and eats them.

Gall crabs live within a chamber in a living coral. A female crab settles in the fork where a branch is forming, and causes the coral to grow over her and form a gall. The gall is like a cage that traps her inside for the rest of her life, but also protects her. An opening allows food particles to enter. Male crabs are small enough to enter the chamber for mating. When the female's eggs hatch, the larvae can escape out of the opening.

Relatives of hermit crabs called squat lobsters (not true lobsters) live mostly in feather stars and sponges. Other hermit crab relatives called porcelain crabs often live in sea anemones, and are immune to their stings.

Some crabs live on land, or even in trees, but they cannot live more than a few miles from the sea. They must keep their gills moist to breathe, and must go to the sea to reproduce. Female land crabs go to the shoreline to deliver their eggs into the ocean. After a period of development in the plankton, the larvae swarm back to the coast, and climb ashore to finish their lives on land.

Some crabs can only mate after the female has climbed out of her shell, and before her new shell has hardened. In some species the female can store the male's sperm for more than a year, and use it whenever she produces another batch of eggs. Female Tanner crabs climb on top of each other to release their eggs, forming mounds over 3' high, containing 200 or more crabs.

Giant land crabs found in Cuba can outrun racehorses!

The arrow crab has a long snout, covered with small hooks, to which food can be attached for later consumption.

A strange animal called the horseshoe crab is not a true crab, but a relative of spiders and scorpions. It lives in the ocean, but comes ashore to lay its eggs on beaches. Horseshoe crabs are considered "living fossils" because they look identical to fossil horseshoe crabs that lived 200 million years ago. They have blue blood from which a product is derived that is used in laboratories to test the purity of drugs and to diagnose diseases.

Luscious Lobsters

We use the word "lobster" to refer to several groups of crustaceans. Like crabs, lobsters have ten legs, but unlike crabs, they have a long flattened abdomen, or "tail," with a fan at the end. Lobsters look like big shrimps with hard shells, but they do not have a shell projection (rostrum) between their eyes.

Clawed lobsters, including Maine lobsters and European lobsters, have large claws on the front legs, that are used for both feeding and defense. Spiny lobsters, found mostly in warmer waters, have no claws, but defend themselves with long antennae that are armored with sharp spines. Slipper lobsters, or shovel-nose lobsters, have neither claws nor hard antennae. Their primary defense is camouflage. All lobsters are scavengers and generalist feeders. They eat worms, mollusks, and crustaceans, including their own kind, if the opportunity arises. If they happen upon a dead fish, mammal, or reptile, they will feed on that, too.

Crustaceans and insects have compound eyes made up of many individual lens units. Maine lobsters have up to 14,000 lenses in each eye. With the compound eyes extended on stalks, lobsters have an extremely wide angle-of-view—nearly all the way around themselves. A new X-ray telescope has been designed, based on the lobster eye, to search a wide arc of the sky.

This female lobster is carrying thousands of tiny orange eggs underneath its abdomen on its "tarspot." The tail fan can be flexed rapidly to propel the lobster backward for a quick escape.

All lobsters are cannibals!

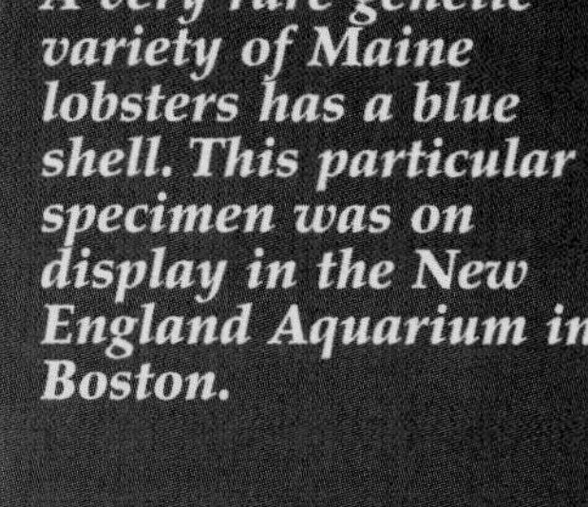

A very rare genetic variety of Maine lobsters has a blue shell. This particular specimen was on display in the New England Aquarium in Boston.

GERARD de NERVAL
(1808- 1855)
PARISIAN POET AND AUTHOR
HAD A PET LOBSTER WHICH HE LED THROUGH THE STREETS OF PARIS ON A LEASH

Believe It or Not!, there is a lobster farm in Portage La Prairie, Canada, in the middle of the Prairies 1500 miles from the Atlantic Ocean.

Until the 20th century, lobsters were considered "poor man's food" in North America. Early colonists fed them to hogs or used them to fertilize their fields. Laws were passed to protect servants from being fed a constant diet of lobsters. Maine lobsters can grow to over 44 lbs. (20 kg), but rarely escape capture for long enough to reach that size anymore.

Spiny lobsters are also fished so heavily in most areas that they rarely reach their maximum size anymore. The great "lobster marches" that were formerly an annual event in Florida, the Bahamas, and the Caribbean, are now rare, with fewer lobsters in the lines. These marches occur when maturing lobsters move from shallow areas where juveniles live, to deeper reefs where adults live. When crossing open areas, the lobsters join together into lines that look like a much larger animal.

A squat lobster conceals itself among the arms of a crinoid, or feather star. The squat lobster matches its color perfectly to that of its host. It gains not only protection, but also free food.

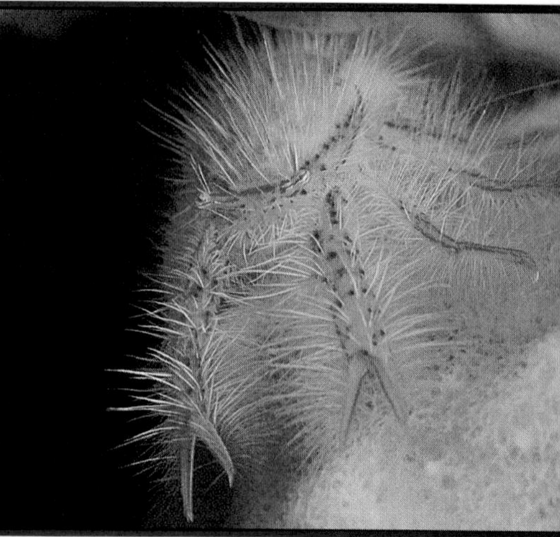

When placed in darkened tanks, marching lobsters continue to march, and orient themselves in a consistent direction with respect to the Earth's magnetic field. Magnetic minerals have been found in their heads. Scientists believe that they use this material as a biological compass for navigation.

Spiny lobsters typically do not have claws, but the long-handed spiny lobster has a curved "false claw" at the end of its first pair of legs.

The large thorny antennae of spiny lobsters are used both as weapons and sense organs. If marching lobsters are attacked, they form a circle, pointing their antennae outward like the spines of a sea urchin. They also use these antennae to feel objects and detect water movements. The smaller antennae, or antennules, detect food and other odors. The bristles on the ends of their legs also serve as organs of smell. They can locate buried food by probing in the sand with their legs.

When lobsters mate, the male deposits his sperm on the female's chest in a black patch called a "tar spot." The sperm can be retained alive for months or even years. When the female is ready to brood a batch of eggs, she scratches the tar spot to release some sperm to fertilize them.

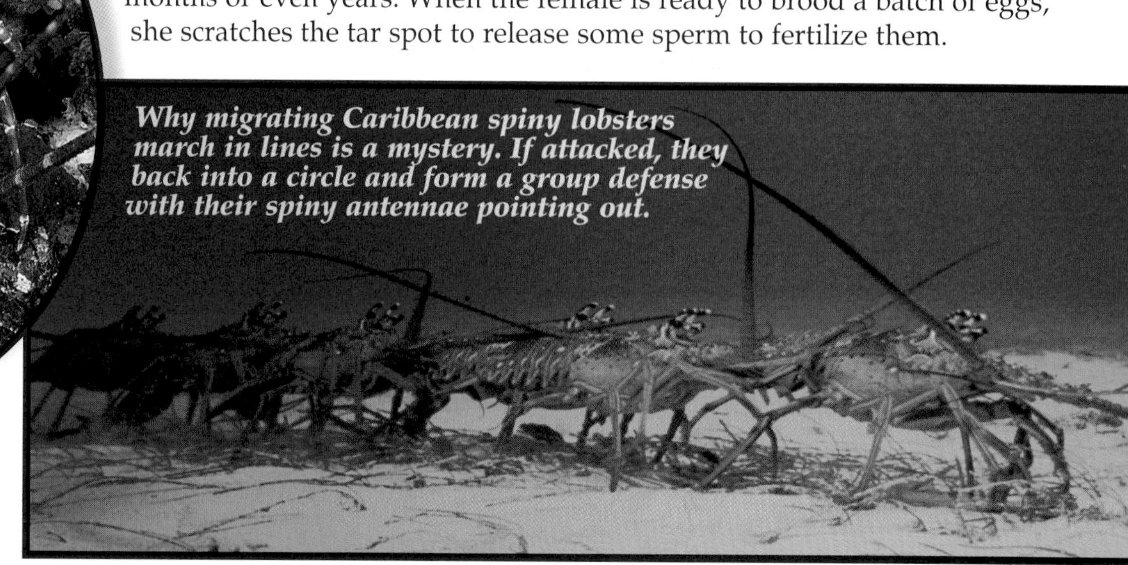

Why migrating Caribbean spiny lobsters march in lines is a mystery. If attacked, they back into a circle and form a group defense with their spiny antennae pointing out.

Beautifully patterned harlequin shrimp live in pairs and feed on much larger sea stars. They may drag an entire sea star to their lair, and consume it bit by bit, or they may sever one arm and take that home.

Shrimpy Shrimps

The animals we call shrimps belong to several different groups of crustaceans. The "true" shrimps are ten-legged crustaceans like crabs and lobsters. Mantis shrimps and opossum shrimps are more distantly related. Most shrimps have shells that are thinner and more flexible than those of crabs and lobsters, a pointy "nose" or rostrum sticking out from their shell, and are smaller than most crabs and lobsters. Shrimp live in a great variety of habitats, including free-swimming in the open ocean. Many of the open-ocean shrimps glow in the dark.

Many shrimps live in close association with other animals. It is not unusual to find shrimps living on the bodies of nudibranchs, sea stars, feather stars, sea cucumbers, sea urchins, sea anemones, corals, sponges, hydroids, or other organisms. Some form close partnerships with other animals on the reef. Partner shrimps share a burrow with a small fish called a goby. The shrimp, which is nearly blind, does all the work of maintaining the burrow, constantly pushing out sand and debris. The goby performs the essential function of "watchdog." It sits alert at the burrow entrance watching for danger. The shrimp keeps one antenna in constant contact with the goby. If the goby darts back down into the burrow, so does the shrimp.

Deep-sea shrimp baffle pursuers by releasing clouds of luminous fluids.

A SHRIMP HAS ITS HEART AND STOMACH IN ITS HEAD

The partner shrimp is nearly blind. It has one antenna touching the "seeing-eye" goby that shares its burrow. If the goby spots danger, the shrimp knows it immediately.

The striped color pattern and long white antennae of the scarlet lady cleaning shrimp serve to advertise its services as a "barber of the reef." The shrimp gets meal delivery, while fish get a "manicure", which includes removal of parasites.

The spotted cleaning shrimp also waves its long antennae to attract customers. When not at work, it retreats within the venomous tentacles of a sea anemone for protection.

Coleman shrimp are usually found in pairs on the surface of a venomous fire urchin. As the urchin moves around the reef, the shrimp move with it.

Other shrimps form temporary partnerships with fish and eels that need help with their personal hygiene. The shrimps operate a service called a cleaning station. Most cleaner shrimps have long white antennae that they wave around to advertise their station (serving the same purpose as a barber pole). Sometimes they also do a little dance to attract customers. Their clients come to the station and usually adopt a special pose to show that they are ready to be cleaned. They will often open their mouths and pop their gill plates open to allow the shrimp full access to all parts of their bodies. The shrimp scampers over its client, removing bits of dead or damaged skin, picking off and eating small parasites, etc. The much larger fish could easily eat the cleaner, but it does not, even when the shrimp goes right inside its mouth.

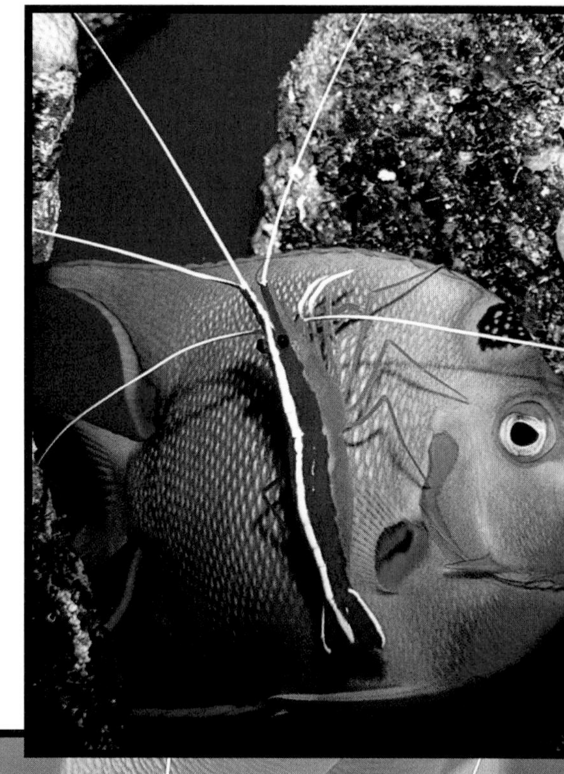

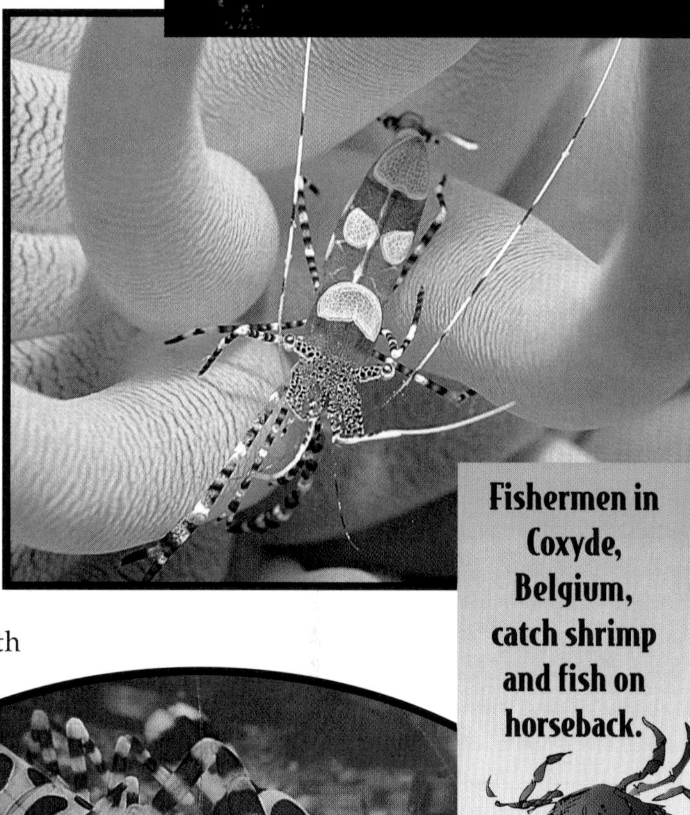

Some pistol shrimps live in sea anemones. They gain the protection of the anemone's stinging tentacles, but they also help to defend the anemone. If the anemone is threatened, the shrimp marches out and snaps its large claw at the intruder. The claw has a trigger mechanism that holds it open while the shrimp's muscles pull against it. When the trigger is released, the claw snaps shut with a loud pop. The noise can be heard by a diver several feet away, and is even heard by sailors through the hulls of their ships. Some pistol shrimps can pop their claws loudly enough to stun small fish, which they then eat.

Fishermen in Coxyde, Belgium, catch shrimp and fish on horseback.

The club-shaped forearm of this mantis shrimp identifies it as a "smasher." It can pulverize the shells of smaller shellfish.

Mantis shrimps lock their claws back like a pistol shrimp. When the claw is released, the victim is either impaled or crushed, depending upon the type of mantis shrimp. Some mantis shrimps are "spearers" and some are "smashers." Spearers have a sharp claw like a spear, and smashers have a blunt claw like a club. Both are fast and deadly. The strike of a mantis shrimp is one of the fastest motions in the animal kingdom. The entire strike takes place in less the 1/200 of a second-faster than the eye can see. The claw can move at speeds up to 400" (1000 cm) per second. Spearers are also known as "thumb splitters" for the damage they can do to marine life collectors. Smashers are known to destroy aquariums by cracking the glass walls!

Mantis shrimps can also injure each other, fighting for burrow space. At mating time, in some species, it is the females that pursue the males, often striking and injuring them.

The shrimp with a built-in searchlight. The Acanthephyra, which inhabits the Atlantic at a depth of 8,000 feet, blinds its enemies in the dark waters by emitting a dazzling flood of light.

Two mantis shrimp fight for possession of a burrow. They will strike each other on the tail until one of them gives up.

GIANT SHRIMP ATTACK! MANTIS SHRIMP IN SAN DIEGO BAY, CALIF., GROW UP TO ONE-FOOT LONG, HAVE RAZOR-SHARP CLAWS THAT RESEMBLE A SWITCH-BLADE AND CAN SLICE HUMAN FLESH TO THE BONE IN 1/200 OF A SECOND

Darn Barnacles

Barnacles are crustaceans that often look like mollusks. Their jointed legs may be hidden by shells, which look like limpet or oyster shells. Like tunicates, barnacles begin life as a free-swimming larva, but soon feel the need to settle down. No respectable adult barnacle wants to be a "drifter," so when maturity approaches, it leaves the plankton, glues its head to the nearest hard surface, and begins to build a limestone house around itself. It spends the rest of its life with its head stuck to a rock kicking its legs around to catch particles of food in the leg hairs.

Rock barnacles have a cone-shaped shell, like a limpet. Gooseneck barnacles have a two-part shell, like an oyster, with a long fleshy stalk. Barnacles attach to almost any object in the water. They can be found on the sea floor, on dock and bridge pilings, on floating debris and on living animals including crabs, turtles, sea cows, and whales. A single whale can carry a ton of barnacles! Barnacles also attach to the undersides of ships. This increases drag, and forces the ship to burn more fuel to move through the water. Barnacles cost the shipping industry billions of dollars each year.

Barnacles can also live as parasites. Many barnacles have evolved to fit the parasitic lifestyle so well that they no longer look anything like crustaceans. They may look more like plants, with long "roots" that reach into the body of their host to draw out nourishment. The "crab-castrating barnacle," invades the bodies of crabs and takes control of their hormones and nervous systems. The crab stops growing so that the barnacle can grow instead. Instead of producing its own eggs, the crab is forced to care for the eggs of the barnacle.

These gooseneck barnacles may look like mollusks, but they are actually crustaceans. Their jointed legs can be seen pulled inside the openings of the shells. When the tidal current flows over them they will use their legs like fishing nets to pull in plankton.

The gooseneck barnacles growing on the shell of this sea turtle will cause a lot of drag when the turtle swims. Some sea turtles have small crabs, which live next to their tail, that help remove barnacles before they can grow large enough to cause a problem.

The jointed legs of barnacles are known as "cirri" or "cirripeds." They move in unison in a fan-like motion to strain plankton from the water.

The barnacle must fertilize her eggs before she gives them to the crab to baby-sit. How can she find a mate while she is living inside the crab's body? Easy—her mate is already living inside her own body. The male exists only as a clump of reproductive cells, which produce sperm for the female's needs.

Barnacles that live in clusters have an easier time finding mates. Connecting with the mate is still a problem though, as the strong glue on its head makes it impossible for the barnacle to leave its shell to go on a date. Barnacles solve this problem with a reproductive organ that is up to five times the animal's body length. Just to be sure that they will be able to reach the right type of partner, most barnacles are both male and female.

Barnacles have no hearts. Their body movements are able to circulate their blood without a special organ for this purpose. They also have no gills, but absorb oxygen through the linings of their shells.

Gooseneck barnacles may cross oceans attached to floating debris. These barnacles are growing on a fishing float.

Parasitic lobster barnacles have red-striped bodies and no shell. They attach to the leg joints, mouth parts, and abdomens of spiny lobsters.

Icky Echinoderms

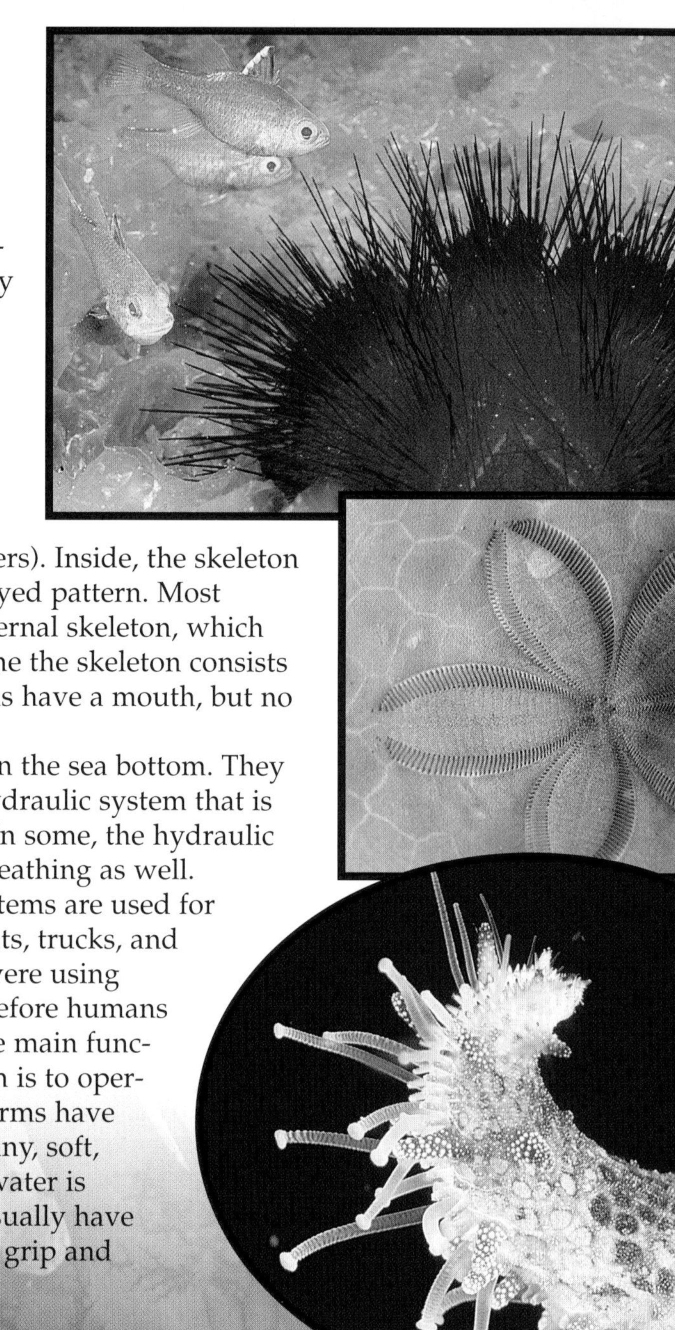

Small fish, such as these cardinalfish, often seek shelter within, or near, the spines of sea urchins.

The five-rayed symmetry of echinoderms is not readily apparent in the body of a living sea biscuit urchin. After death, however, the skeleton reveals five petal-shaped loops of gill openings.

As a moving sea star extends an arm forward, the tube feet reach outward searching for a surface to grip. Each tube foot has a suction cup at the end, which can stick tightly to the seafloor, or to a food item.

Sea stars, sea urchins, sea cucumbers, sand dollars, feather stars, brittle stars, sea biscuits and basket stars all belong to the group of animals known as echinoderms (ee-KINE-o-dermz). These are evolutionarily advanced invertebrates, which may have given rise to the vertebrates. The "trademark" of the echinoderms is a five-rayed body plan. Sometimes this is obvious from the outside (as in a five-armed sea star), and sometimes not (as in sea cucumbers). Inside, the skeleton and organs will reveal the five-rayed pattern. Most echinoderms have a complete internal skeleton, which shows the star pattern, but in some the skeleton consists only of tiny spicules. Echinoderms have a mouth, but no head, and no brain or heart.

Nearly all echinoderms live on the sea bottom. They move around with the aid of a hydraulic system that is unique to this group of animals. In some, the hydraulic system is used for feeding and breathing as well. Hydraulic, or water pressure, systems are used for steering and other controls in boats, trucks, and heavy machinery. Echinoderms were using hydraulics for millions of years before humans came up with the idea. One of the main functions of the water pressure system is to operate their tube feet. Most echinoderms have hundreds or thousands of these tiny, soft, projections, which extend when water is forced into them. The tube feet usually have suction cup ends so that they can grip and attach to objects.

The Astrophyton verrucosum muelleri starfish–belonging to the Euryale family–can have as many as 81,920 tube feet

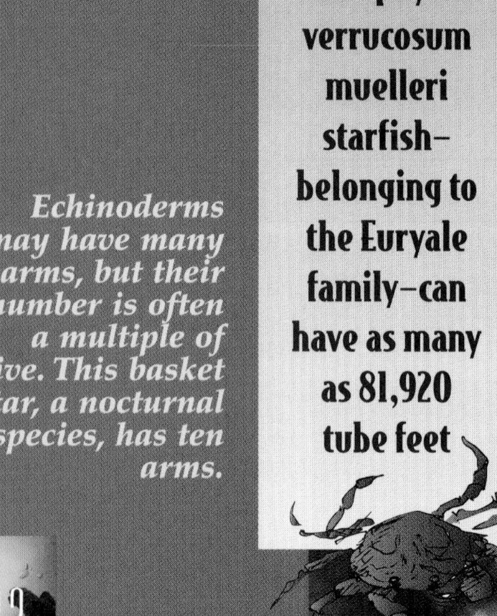

Echinoderms may have many arms, but their number is often a multiple of five. This basket star, a nocturnal species, has ten arms.

This rainbow sea star is not as strong as the clam upon which it is feeding, but it can grip the clam's shell with its tube feet and pull for hours until it opens the shell wide enough to slip its stomach inside.

A starfish can turn its stomach inside out!

SUPER STARS

Sea stars are not fish, so scientists do not call them starfish. It may appear that they do not do much, but that is only because we live on a different time scale. If films of them are speeded up, they can be seen to have active lives. They also have remarkable abilities. For one thing, they can see with their feet! Sea stars have no heads and no true eyes, but many have eyespots, which can detect light and darkness. These are found on the tube feet at the ends of their arms.

Sea stars have an amazing ability to recover from injuries. If an arm is lost, they can grow a new arm. In some kinds, an arm that has broken off can grow a whole new body! Most sea stars have five arms, but some kinds have up to fifty.

Sea stars also have incredible endurance. Many kinds prey on clams, oysters, and other shelled animals. Clams can hold their shells so tightly shut that almost nothing can pry them open, but a sea star can attach its tube feet to the outside of the shell and pull steadily until the clam tires and a gap is opened. The sea star then pushes its stomach out of its body and into the clamshell to digest the clam.

The name "echinoderm" means "spiny skin." It is particularly appropriate for long-spined sea urchins, but almost all echinoderms have some kind of skin armor.

Sea stars have amazing powers of regeneration. The rainbow sea star on the right is starting to regrow all its arms from only a small piece of the central disc.

A tiny juvenile black sea urchin explores the body of a much larger relative—a purple sea star.

Echinoderms

Some sea stars, such as the giant sunflower star from Alaska, feed on other sea stars. The sunflower star has been flipped upside down in order to show the arm of the other star going into its mouth.

Sea stars are often collected as curios, but the brilliant colors seen in this living specimen usually fade quickly when the star is dried.

Crown-of-thorns sea stars feed on coral in the same way. They crawl on top of a coral head and spread their stomach over it. They digest the coral polyps and leave only a dead white skeleton. Sometimes hundreds or thousands of these stars suddenly appear on a reef, nearly wiping out all of the corals. This appears to be part of a natural cycle, but some people believe that it happens more often now, due to human impact on the environment. The crown-of-thorns is dangerous to humans, too. It has hard, sharp spines armed with venom that can inflict a painful injury if stepped on.

Other sea stars eat sponges, worms, snails, crabs, or other echinoderms. Sun stars swallow spiny sea urchins whole and spit out the shell after the animal has been digested. Some stars can even attack and consume sleeping fish! Sea stars can reproduce by splitting apart, by casting off arms that grow into new stars, or by releasing eggs and sperm into the water.

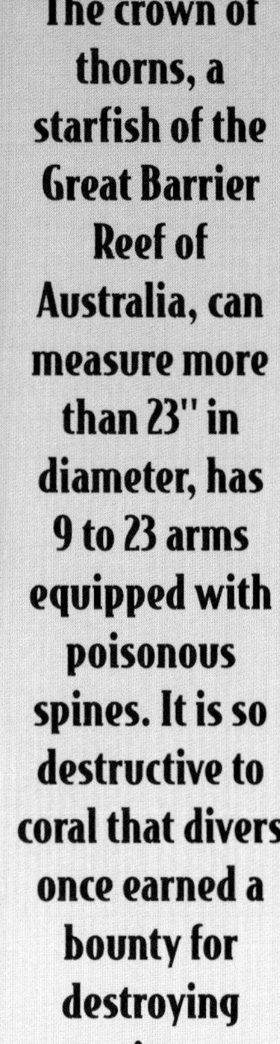

The crown of thorns, a starfish of the Great Barrier Reef of Australia, can measure more than 23" in diameter, has 9 to 23 arms equipped with poisonous spines. It is so destructive to coral that divers once earned a bounty for destroying it.

The crown-of-thorns sea star, although a coral-killer, can be quite beautiful.

The spines covering the body of this young crown of thorns sea star are covered with toxic mucus. Accidental contact with one of these animals can cause a puncture wound that is not only painful, but will produce a festering sore that is very slow to heal.

The snakelike arms of brittle stars are distinct from the body disc, and can be whipped around for rapid locomotion.

The ten-rayed pattern on the body disc of this brittle star follows the echinoderm "multiples of five" rule.

Brittle and Basket Stars

Brittle stars look something like sea stars, but have a body disc that is distinct from the arms. In sea stars, the body tapers out to form the arms. The arms of brittle stars are thinner and more flexible than those of sea stars. Brittle stars walk by flexing their arms, while most sea stars keep their arms stiff, and use their tube feet to move them along.

Brittle stars get their name because they come apart very easily when handled. Actually they are not brittle—they just have a very effective defense mechanism. When attacked, they cast off one or more of their arms. The discarded arm wriggles around, and keeps the attention of the predator while the brittle star escapes. The arm will grow back later. Like most echinoderms, brittle stars are most active at night. During the day they hide under rocks or in other dark places.

One kind of brittle star hides deep inside holes under coral ledges. At night only the arms reach out from the holes. Flashes of green light run up and down the arms, especially if they are touched. Perhaps this is a way to attract plankton for food, or to startle predators.

Basket stars are close relatives of brittle stars. They feed only at night. They climb on top of the nearest high object and spread their arms out to catch plankton. Their arms are branched so many times that the basket star looks like a lace tablecloth.

During the day, basket stars coil up and hide under ledges or in the branches of corals or any place where they will not be noticed. A basket star, measuring 3' (1 m) across at night, can become a ball the size of your fist by day.

These miniature basket stars cling tightly to their host sponge by day, but at night they will unfurl and stretch out their arms to capture plankton from the water currents.

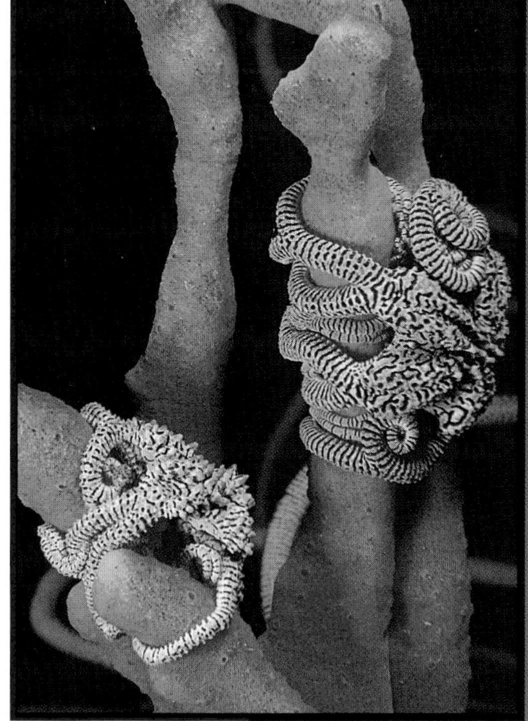

Creepy Cucumbers

Sea cucumbers have been called the "street cleaners" of the undersea city. They creep slowly across the bottom, sweeping or "vacuuming" up debris and extracting the food value from it. Some kinds just push themselves through the sand, with the sand going into the mouth at one end and coming out the other. If there is anything in the sand that can be digested, the sea cucumber makes use of it. A few kinds of sea cucumbers use lacy tentacles to filter plankton out of the water.

Sea cucumbers look more like slugs or vegetables than stars, but their five-rayed symmetry can be seen in their internal organs, and sometimes in the tentacles around their heads. Since they are slow moving and usually out in the open, it is not surprising that many kinds are poisonous. The spiky spicules in their skin can also make them unpleasant to eat. However, humans, especially in Asia, eat several kinds.

Some sea cucumbers grow special sticky threads inside. When disturbed, they squirt the threads out their rear. The threads can entangle a predator, and are sometimes poisonous.

Most sea cucumbers reproduce by releasing eggs and sperm into the water. When the time is right, each cucumber rises up like a cobra and releases a milky fluid out of a hole on top of its head.

Sea cucumbers range in size from about ½" (1 cm) to over 6' (2 m) in length. They are common on shallow reefs, mud flats, and sand plains. They are even more common in the very deep sea. Sea cucumbers often serve as "mobile homes" for other creatures. Shrimp and crabs may live on their skin, or inside the mouth. An odd fish, called the pearl fish, lives inside of sea cucumbers. It only comes out at night to feed. It has a sharp, pointed tail.

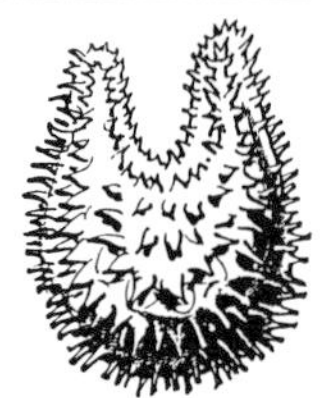

THE SEA CUCUMBER CAN RESTORE ANY PART OF ITS BODY THAT HAS BEEN DAMAGED, INCLUDING THE STICKY "THREADS" OR CUVIERIAN TUBULES, IT EXTRUDES TO WARD OFF PREDATORS

The sea cucumber, when attacked by a lobster or other predator, defends itself by expelling its own digestive system—in which the attacker becomes entangled. The sea cucumber then grows another digestive system.

The "candy-cane sea cucumber" has only recently been scientifically described and named. Its protective spines are unusually sharp for a sea cucumber.

The sticky threads coming out of this sea cucumber are called "tubules of Cuvier." A predator will become entangled in the threads, allowing the cucumber to escape while the predator frees itself.

Some urchins have strong, stout spines, while others have thin brittle spines that penetrate an attacker more easily, and may break off inside the wound.

The sea urchin (Echinus) is encased in a round shell—yet it can climb a vertical wall of rock.

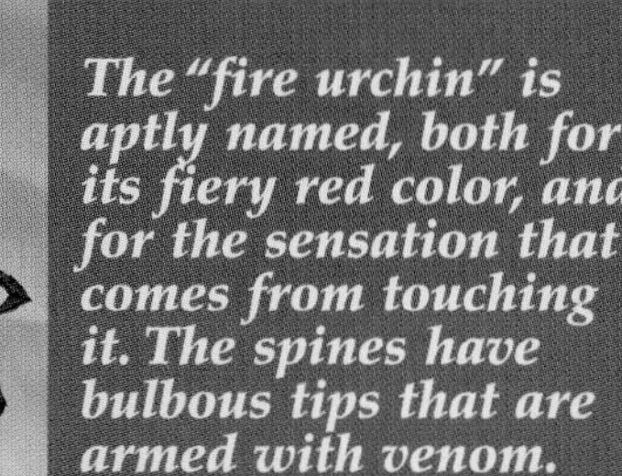

Ugly Urchins

Sea urchins look like pincushions. The spines often have very sharp tips and tiny barbs on the sides. If you touch one, the spine can break off, and work its way into your flesh. A poison often causes a painful reaction that may lead to an infection. Not all urchins are dangerous though. Some have spines that are blunt or very short.

Sand dollars, sea biscuits and heart urchins are all short-spined sea urchins that live under the sand. They are rarely seen alive, but after they die we often find their shells or skeletons along the shore. In the dead skeletons the five-rayed pattern that is hidden by the spine during life is clearly visible.

The "fire urchin" is aptly named, both for its fiery red color, and for the sensation that comes from touching it. The spines have bulbous tips that are armed with venom.

THE COMMON SEA URCHIN WHICH CAN WALK ON ITS SPINES AS WELL AS ITS LEGS MAY HAVE AS MANY AS 1,860 LEGS AND 4,000 SPINES

Slate pencil sea urchins grow in shallow water and may be briefly exposed at very low tides. Sometimes their blunt spines are collected to make wind chimes.

The mouth of a sea urchin is hidden on the underside.

Several kinds of carrier urchins use their tube feet to hold bits of seaweed or other material to camouflage themselves. Some have even been seen carrying around beer cans and other trash!

Sea urchins are not vicious animals. In fact, they eat a mostly vegetarian diet. They scrape algae from the sea floor with the jaws on the underside of their bodies. Sea urchin jaws are among the most complex jaws in the animal kingdom. There are up to 60 different muscles working the jaws, and they are strong enough to bore through rock.

The spines are needed for self-defense, because many animals find the internal organs of sea urchins quite delicious. This includes humans, especially in Asia, where the reproductive organs of sea urchins often end up in sushi. Fish that like to eat urchins can often be recognized by lips that are stained purple from all the spines that have stuck them. Longnose butterflyfish have a long snout that they use like tweezers to reach in between the spines and pluck off tube feet to eat. Some small fish hide between the spines of sea urchins. In some cases they repay the favor of protection by cleaning parasites off the urchin.

Some sea urchins also defend themselves with tiny pincers that are found between the spines. In flower urchins, these pincers are so venomous that a sting can be very painful, and sometimes even fatal.

Some urchins have various size spines.

Feather Stars and Sea Lilies

Imagine plucking a handful of the most brightly colored feathers from each of the most beautiful kinds of parrots and macaws. Pinch the feathers together at the quills, and bend them outward in a circle. You would have something that looks very much like a feather star. The sticky arms trap plankton from the currents. They are so effective that small crustaceans and fish often live inside of them to take advantage of their food-gathering abilities. The branched arms of the feather star also provide a great place for these creatures to hide from predators. They usually match their color pattern exactly to that of the feather star so that they are almost invisible.

Feather stars can scuttle around the reef surprisingly quickly. Many kinds hide inside the coral by day, and crawl out at night to perch themselves on top of the highest part of the reef to filter-feed. Some kinds can swim awkwardly by waving their arms.

Relatives of feather stars, called sea lilies, found in the deep sea, are less able to move around. Their arms are supported on top of a stalk. Together, feather stars and sea lilies are known as crinoids. Crinoids have been living in the ocean for 600 million years. They are among the most ancient of the creatures of the reef, as well as among the most beautiful.

This feather star shrimp has perfectly camouflaged itself to match the color of its host. It obtains both shelter and food from the feather star on which it lives.

Jointed "legs" called cirri on the underside of a feather star enable it to grasp its host. This feather star has climbed up on some red finger sponges and wrapped its cirri around them.

Crinoids are one of the oldest life forms in the world, dating back 600 million years.

Mysterious Mollusks

Many giant clams have blue-patterned mantles. The shell of this giant clam is hidden in a clump of finger coral, but its brilliant blue-splotched mantle is exposed.

This nudibranch is raising its head to detect food scents in the water currents with the horn-like sensory organs on its head. The branching plume on its back, at mid-body, is its gills.

There are an estimated 100, 000 different species of mollusks (or molluscs). Many mollusks look very different from each other, but they all have a few characteristics in common. Mollusks have soft bodies, which they protect with a hard shell or shells. Usually the animal lives inside the shell, but sometimes the shell is hidden inside its body. In some mollusks the shell has become very small during the course of evolution, or has disappeared entirely. Other general characteristics of mollusks include a fold of flesh that secretes the shell, called the mantle, and a muscular foot. Most mollusks have a feeding structure called a radula. The radula resembles a rasp, with many small teeth. It can be considered the "tongue" of the mollusk. Some species have as many as 750,000 teeth on this tongue, and can use it to cut like a chain saw!

Murex satatailis, a mollusk of Senegal, Africa, to close the opening in its shell, secretes a substance which is distilled to produce one of India's most expensive perfumes.

THE LEAPING SHELL

FILE CLAMS, OR "FLAME SCALLOPS," A TYPE OF MOLLUSK, CAN LEAP 14 INCHES

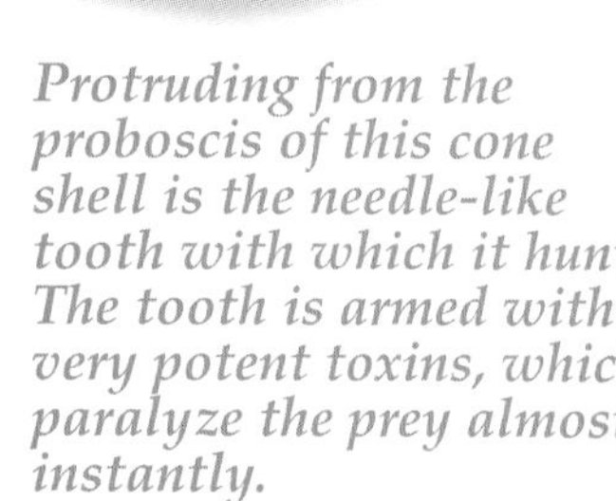

Protruding from the proboscis of this cone shell is the needle-like tooth with which it hunt The tooth is armed with very potent toxins, whic paralyze the prey almost instantly.

Sneaky Snails

Snails have a single shell with a "trap door" to close the opening. The shell grows outward in a spiral, which enlarges to make room for the animal as it grows.

There may be as many as 75,000 different kinds of snails and slugs, so there is a great deal of variety. Some snail shells are among the most beautiful objects in nature, and can be worth hundreds or even thousands of dollars to collectors. A live snail may look nothing like its preserved shell, though. Often the shell is hidden by the living mantle of the snail, or covered by growths of other organisms. Snail shells are used by people for ornaments, tools, musical instruments, and food. Some types, such as abalone, are expensive gourmet foods. In some island nations, snail shells are traditionally used as money. In some areas, some snails are in danger of being wiped out due to over-collection by people.

Largest ammonites in the world. Two giant fossil sea snails found in a quarry in Seppenrade, Germany each weigh 7,700 pounds.

Just as there is great variety in how snails look, there are great differences in how they live. Most snails crawl upon the sea floor, or upon other sea creatures, but violet snails float in the open ocean. They build rafts out of mucus bubbles to support them as they drift around searching for their prey—the deadly Portuguese man-of-war and its relatives.

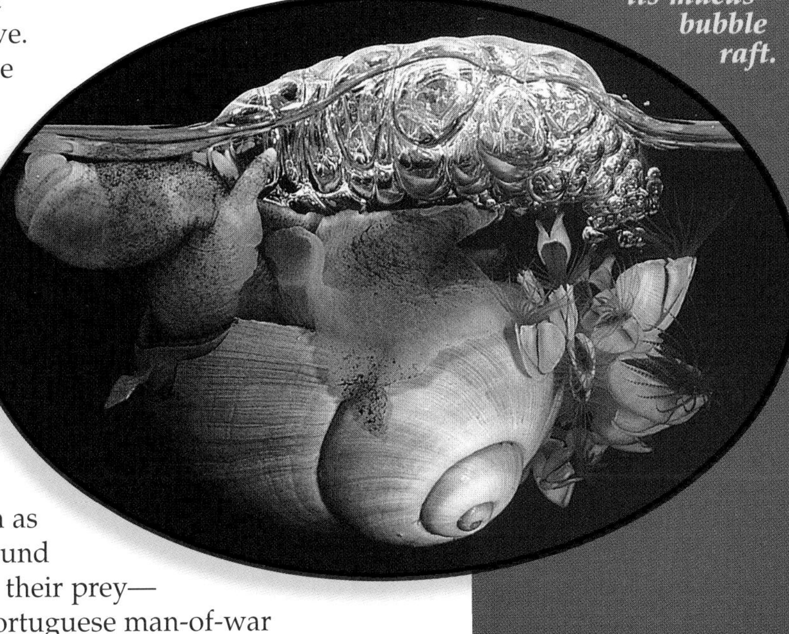

The violet snail spends its entire life at sea yet, as an adult, is unable to swim! It will sink if dislodged from its mucus bubble raft.

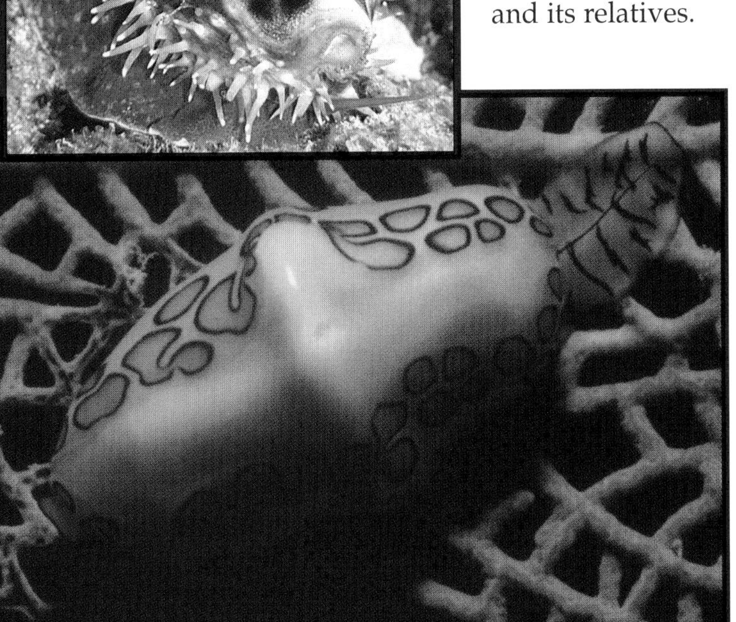

The tiger cowry moves by gliding on its dark, muscular foot (at bottom).

While feeding the spotted mantle of a flamingo tongue snail covers its shell. Divers and snorkelers who collect these beautiful animals are inevitably disappointed when the animal decays, leaving only a dull cream-colored shell.

Three golden wentletrap snails are feeding on a colony of orange cup corals. The snails have extended their siphons inside the coral skeletons to reach the polyps.

Limpets are also known as "Chinaman's hat" shells, because of the conical shape of the shells of these snails. They can often be seen stuck to rocks at low tide.

This cone shell has its proboscis extended. Many cone shells have beautifully patterned shells, but collecting or handling them can be a fatal mistake.

Limpets, nerites, conchs, and periwinkles crawl around slowly, grazing on algae. Worm snails catch floating food particles with mucus nets. Other snails are active predators. Helmet shells scoot along the sea floor. When they find a sea urchin, they rear up and pounce on it. Auger shells feed mainly on worms. Trumpet shells eat urchins, sea cucumbers and sea stars, including the crown-of-thorns sea star with its venomous spines. Collecting of trumpet shells for their large beautiful shells can be a hazard to coral reefs, as it removes the main enemy of the coral-eating crown-of-thorns.

Some sea snails actually eat corals. The purple snail, Drupella, has destroyed whole reefs. Many snails prey on other mollusks. Some whelks and murex shells drill holes through the shells of oysters and other mollusks. Then they pump in chemicals that digest and liquefy the flesh of their victim so they can suck it out.

Cone shells are among the most dangerous animals in the ocean. Some kinds carry enough venom to kill several humans. People who have picked up the small, beautifully patterned shells have been killed when the snail's flexible "harpoon gun" reached out of the tip of the shell and fired its poison dart into their fingers. Normally cone shells use their venomous darts to subdue other shells, worms, and fish. Some hunt fish that are larger and stronger than themselves, so the poison must be very strong to paralyze the prey quickly before it escapes.

The largest snails called conchs *(pronounced konks)* are the only animals in the ocean to get around by hopping. When a conch senses a cone shell approaching, it may jump backward completely off the bottom, to get away. Some cowrie shells can break off part of their foot when seized by a predator, just as a lizard casts off its tail to escape. Some murex and drupe shells defend themselves with toxic chemicals. These are marked with bright dyes that the Greeks and Romans used to use to dye their robes. The purple-dye murex produces a dye that was so prized it was reserved for royalty, and known as "royal purple."

Many snails live on other animals for their whole lives. Their hosts include sea stars, sea cucumbers, sea urchins, and other snails. In some cases they live as parasites, consuming their host's tissues or body fluids. In other cases they feed on cast-off skin, mucus, or feces from their host, or merely use it for shelter and transportation. Vampire snails do not live on their hosts, but only approach them when they are asleep. A long feeding tube pierces the victim's skin, and sucks out blood or body fluids. Various kinds of vampire snails attack parrot fish, sharks and even electric rays!

The stalked eyes of a queen conch peer out cautiously from under its shell. Queen conch are extremely popular for food throughout the West Indies. As a result, their numbers have been greatly reduced, and they have even been completely eliminated from some parts of their range.

Vampire snails are among the few animals in the ocean unafraid to taste the blood of a living shark. This one is using its proboscis to investigate a resting nurse shark, which may become its next meal.

The smooth turban shell spends most of its life in the kelp forest, high above the sea floor. This one is using its bright red foot to hold onto a giant kelp plant.

Unblemished shells sold in shell shops have usually been taken from live animals, threatening the survival of populations of these mollusks. Shells found washed up on the beach may have imperfections, but collecting them does not damage the marine ecosystem.

The moon snail eats clams by drilling a hole in their shells with its tongue!

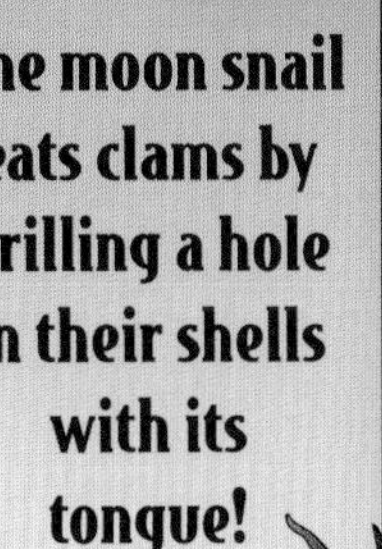

Slimy Sea Slugs

Slugs are snails that have lost their shells through evolution. Sea slugs look very much like land slugs except for their colors. Many sea slugs have colors that look like they came from the "psychedelic" 60s.

Bright colors are often a warning that there is something nasty inside. The color patterns of sea slugs are announcements of toxic or distasteful chemicals. With either no shell to protect their soft bodies, or only a small internal shell, they rely heavily on their chemical defense system. Most sea slugs obtain their defensive chemicals from their food, particularly sponges. Some slugs also absorb the color of the sponge they eat, so that they become almost invisible while they are resting on the sponge. Sea hares (a type of large sea slug) can squirt a purple cloud of foul tasting chemicals into the water when they are disturbed. Sidegill slugs can release sulfuric acid when they are disturbed.

Some sea slugs carry stinging weapons that they obtain from their food. They eat hydroids and other cnidarians without digesting the cnidae. The cnidae enter quill-like extensions on the slug's backs, and are used for defense. Some slugs are able to capture the zooxanthellae from cnidarians and farm them for food. Other sea slugs feed on plants. Some are able to capture the plant cells that perform photosynthesis. When they move these onto their backs (where they can receive sunlight), the cells produce food for the sea slug, just as they did for the plant. Solar-powered sea slugs may not set any speed records, but they can go farther with less food than they could without their "photo cells."

The sea star (right) eats other mollusks but will not consume the white sea slug (nudibranch), because of its protective toxic slime.

The bright yellow spots on the "fried egg nudibranch" may be warning signals for its chemical defense system. The sea slug is also known as the "sticky finger nudibranch" because the noxious chemicals leave a strong odor if handled.

The eggs of the Spanish dancer nudibranch are laid in a ribbon that looks like pink chiffon, and can contain thousands of eggs. Fish will not eat these eggs probably due to chemical defenses.

The most colorful of the sea slugs are the nudibranchs, or "naked lungs." Nudibranchs have their gills ("wet lungs") exposed on top of their bodies. Some also have other projections on their backs. Sometimes these are used like gills for breathing. They may also carry defensive weapons or chemicals. One or more pairs of "horns" on the head serve as organs of smell, taste and touch. Most nudibranchs are small, but Tochuina tetraquetra can grow to over 2.2 pounds, and is eaten in Russia. One type of sea hare grows even larger—to over 4½ pounds. It is poisonous, but some smaller varieties are eaten in the South Pacific.

Like other slugs, nudibranchs usually get around on their foot, creeping across a layer of slime they produce. However, some can also swim awkwardly. The man-of-war nudibranch spends its life in the open ocean, floating on the surface, and feeding on man-of-war jellies and other floating creatures.

All nudibranchs are carnivores (meat-eaters). Some feed on other nudibranchs, including their own kind. Some nudibranchs carry "hitchhikers"—small shrimps that ride on their backs. The shrimp eat their feces, bits of skin and mucus, and parasites.

Nudibranchs are both male and female at the same time. When they mate, each partner performs the roles of both sexes. After mating, both partners lay delicate ribbons of eggs. When the eggs hatch, each releases a planktonic larva, which does not resemble the adult. The larvae, unlike the adult, have shells, showing their relationship to true snails.

When two nudibranchs of the same species meet on the reef, they will usually mate. Since they are both male and female at the same time, every member of their species is a prospective mate.

After mating, each nudibranch lays thousands of tiny eggs, glued together in a spiral ribbon.

Two nudibranchs feed on a colony of bryozoans or "moss animals." Most nudibranchs are carnivores, but some types of sea slugs are herbivores.

The Spanish shawl nudibranch feeds on stinging hydroids. The bright orange color of the projections on its back is probably a warning to other animals of stinging cells, which it has stored in these projections for its own defense.

The shell of the tridacna clam measuring 5 feet in length is used by children on the Mollucas archipelago as a bathtub.

Bountiful Bivalves

Clams are mollusks that live between two shells that are joined at a hinge on one side. Scientists call clams and their relatives "bivalves," meaning "two shells." Oysters, mussels, scallops, file shells, pen shells, ark shells, purse shells, and ship worms are all "bivalves." The two shells of bivalves are usually similar, but they are not always exactly alike. The shells function both as a suit of armor (for protection) and a skeleton (a hard surface to which the muscles can attach).

Bivalves have strong muscles that hold the two shells together except when they are opened to draw in water for breathing, feeding or swimming. The body is similar to a snail or slug, except bivalves have no heads. Some do have eyes, though. Scallops have a whole row of eyes along each lip of the two shells. The eyes can detect the shadow of an approaching predator, and signal the shell to snap shut. The gills of bivalves are used for both breathing and feeding. Bivalves feed by filtering plankton and food particles from the water. Oysters and clams can pump over 390 gallons (1500 liters) of water a day through their shells. That is about 1,000 times as much water as the average person drinks in a day.

Some bivalves, like clams, live buried in sand or mud. Others attach themselves to the sea floor or other surfaces. They do this either by gluing one shell to a hard surface, or by attaching strong threads to the surface. Some bivalves bore into stone or coral to make a home for themselves.

Despite legendary stories of divers getting their arms or legs caught in "man- eating" clams, the giant Tridacna clam closes so slowly, divers really have very little to fear from these 3-foot long, 500 pound shells.

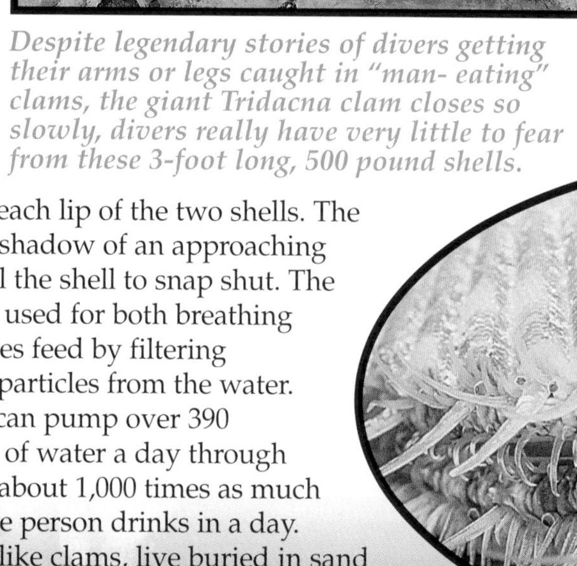

Tridacna clams grow so large that their shells can be used as bathtubs for babies. The baby and clam shown here were featured in a Ripley drawing in 1935.

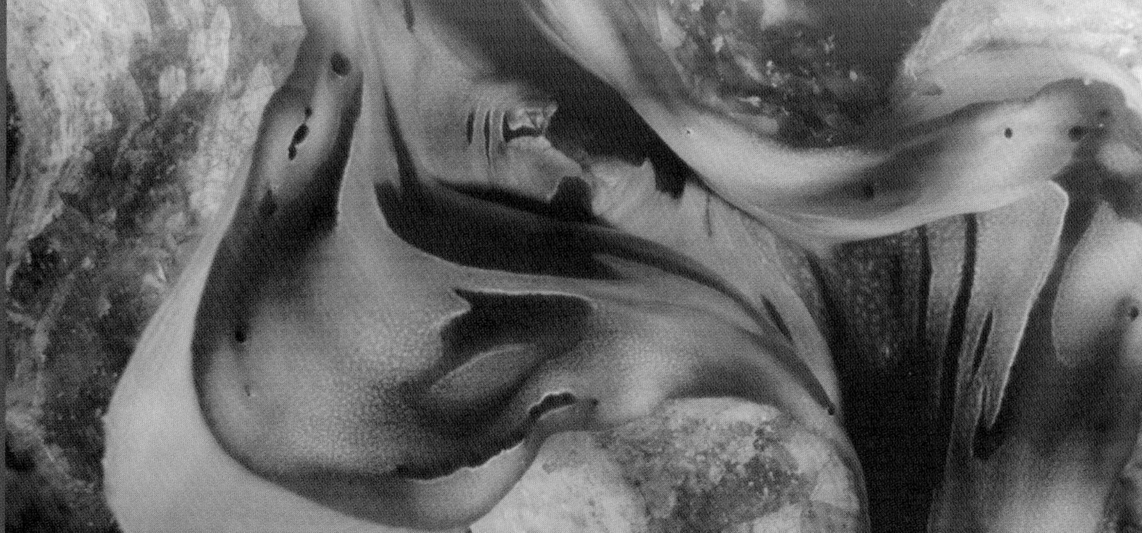

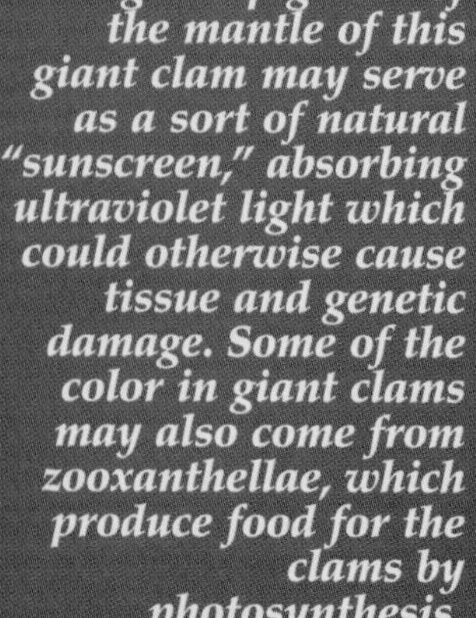

The green pigment of the mantle of this giant clam may serve as a sort of natural "sunscreen," absorbing ultraviolet light which could otherwise cause tissue and genetic damage. Some of the color in giant clams may also come from zooxanthellae, which produce food for the clams by photosynthesis.

Bivalves range in size from tiny shells only ½" (1 ml) across to giant clams more than a 3' (1 m) in length, and weighing up to 880 pounds (400 kg). Contrary to old movies and legends, giant clams rarely trap divers' hands or feet. By the time they reach a large size, they contain so much flesh that their shells are unable to snap completely shut quickly. Giant clams sometimes have small fish and shrimp living on the surface of their bodies. They also have other more important partners. Like corals, giant clams farm zooxanthellae within their bodies to produce food. They are found mostly in shallow water because their zooxanthellae need light for photosynthesis. Too much sunlight, however, can harm the clam, just as it can cause sunburn and cancer in humans (and bleaching in corals). Giant clams have pigments that color their mantles in a different pattern for nearly every clam. These pigments may help to protect them from sun damage.

Thorny oysters are common on coral reefs, but are very hard to see. They are usually completely covered with sponges and other growths. Scientists believe that the main purpose of the spines on the oyster's shell is to attract sponges. The sponges both conceal the oyster from predators and protect it with their toxic chemicals.

The Royal Glutton. Emperor Vitellius (15 – 69) of Rome ate 1200 oysters in one meal.

A thorny oyster has its shells wide open, revealing the distinctive pattern on the mantle.

A close-up of the mantle of a variable thorny oyster shows the distinctive white mottling on an orange background. The least disturbance will cause the shell to snap shut.

The two rows of blue eyes along the lips of a scallop's shell do not form images. They merely detect changes in the amount of light. The shadow of an approaching predator causes the shell to snap shut before it can be attacked.

Most people who eat oysters will never find a pearl in one, but Carol Joan Farol of New Orleans once found 106 pearls in one oyster! (1933)

The "flame scallop" is not a true scallop, but a related bivalve properly known as a file shell.

Believe It or Not!, there is a museum in France dedicated to oysters, with special displays featuring culinary recipes!

Bivalves, like other mollusks, have planktonic larvae that drift and swim in the currents. As adults, most of them do not move much. Giant clams are too heavy, and oysters have one shell glued to the bottom. Bivalves that attach themselves with threads can sometimes move a little by lifting off threads, and then re-attaching them. Clams that burrow in the bottom sand can move around underneath the sand. Surf clams use waves to propel themselves to and from shore as the tide goes in and out. They actually surf in toward the beach. Scallops and file shells can escape danger by clapping their shells together like castanets, jumping backward with each clap.

Bivalves live in nearly every part of the ocean, from the tropics to the arctic, and from the beach down to the very deepest parts, including deep-sea volcanic vents. Vent clams obtain nourishment from sulfur-eating bacteria that grow in the hot vent water. Some deep-sea clams grow very slowly, taking 100 years to add ⅓" (1 cm) in length. Arctic clams also grow slowly, and may live more than 200 years.

The shells of most bivalves are coated on the inside with a glossy material called mother of pearl, which makes a smooth, comfortable home for the mollusk's soft body. In some types, if a bit of irritating material gets inside the shell, the mollusk coats it with mother of pearl. After some layers are added, it becomes a pearl. Pearl farmers deliberately place bits of broken shell inside of oysters to cause pearls to grow.

The natives of Comodoro Rivadavia, Argentina, build houses out of tremendous mounds of prehistoric oyster shells.

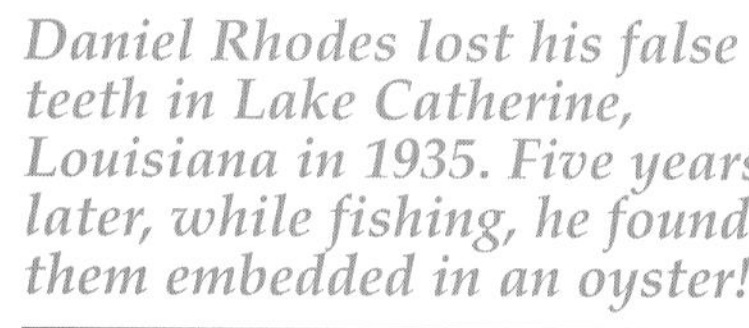

The flesh of giant clams is not only beautifully colored, but highly edible. As a result, giant clam populations have been greatly reduced or eliminated from most areas where they formerly occurred in abundance.

Daniel Rhodes lost his false teeth in Lake Catherine, Louisiana in 1935. Five years later, while fishing, he found them embedded in an oyster!

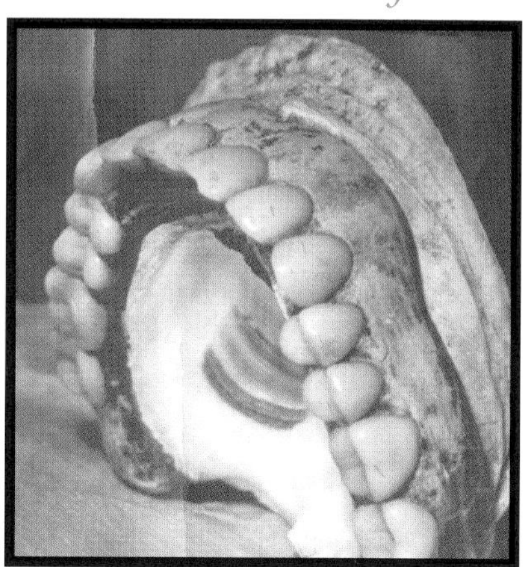

When it comes to reproduction, bivalves are real champions. Oysters can produce up to 100 million eggs in a single season. They boost their success by changing back andforth from male to female.

In most cases the fertilized egg becomes a larva which floats in the plankton for a couple of weeks before settling onto the sea floor. In freshwater mussels the egg develops within the mother into a larva which looks like a tiny clam with teeth on the edges of the shell. When the larvae are ejected from the mother, they "bite down" onto the fins or scales of a fish, then burrow into its flesh. The mussels live as parasites on the fish for weeks before they fall to the stream-bed to live as adults. During their parasitic phase, the mussel larvae travel wherever the fish swims. In this way they can "hitchhike" many miles up streams!

The swan mussel often uses a small fish called a bitterling to nourish and transport its young. The bitterling uses the swan mussel in the same way. The female bitterling deposits her eggs inside the mussel through a long tube. A male bitterling then ejects his sperm over the mussel, so that it is drawn inside to fertilize the eggs. At the same time, the mussel ejects its larvae, which attach to the bitterlings. The mussel larvae develop within the bitterlings, while the bitterling eggs develop within the mussel.

Swedish fisherman Peder Carlsson found an engagement ring inside a mussel, and was able to return it to its owner who had lost it two years earlier!

The shell of this honeycomb oyster is completely covered by encrusting sponges and other organisms. Only the zigzag opening reveals its identity.

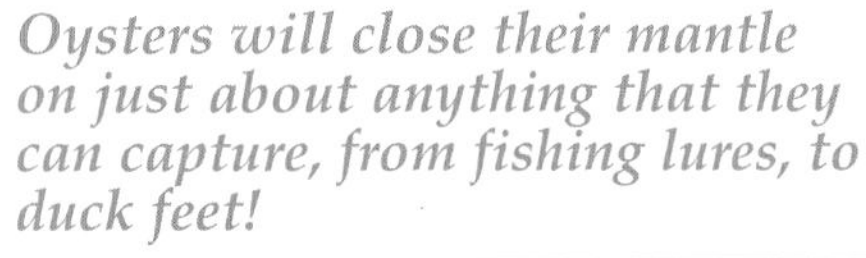
Oysters will close their mantle on just about anything that they can capture, from fishing lures, to duck feet!

Cerebral Cephalopods

Only a few types of octopus spend their lives in open ocean. Although all octopuses can swim by jet propulsion, most prefer to stay close to the seafloor.

The chambered nautilus is designed so that it can move around just by breathing. Water circulated over the gills is forced out through the jet propulsion siphon, moving the animal backward at about an inch per second.

The eyes of octopuses are able to focus, and to adapt to changes in light levels. The similarity between the eyes of cephalopods and vertebrates is considered to be a case of convergent evolution.

Perhaps the most remarkable mollusks are the cephalopods (SEF-uh-lo-pods), including octopus, squid, cuttlefish, and nautilus. The name comes from the Greek words for "head" and "foot." In cephalopods the foot has evolved into arms and tentacles, which attach to a large head. They have the largest brains of any invertebrates. The brain is protected by a skull of cartilage. Cephalopods are capable of complex behaviors, and appear to be as intelligent as many reptiles and mammals. This is especially amazing considering that many have very short lives—often only one to two years, allowing little time for learning. Cephalopods have well-developed eyesight and other senses. The eyes of squid, octopus, and cuttlefish are large, complex, and strikingly similar to our own. In this case, evolution produced almost identical results twice in groups of organisms which are not related (mollusks and vertebrates). In most cephalopods, evolution has resulted in a shell that is small and hidden inside the body, or has disappeared entirely.

"The Saint Augustine Sea Monster." In 1896, the remains of a sea creature, believed at the time to be a giant octopus with 32 foot long tentacles, washed up on the beach in St. Augustine, Florida!

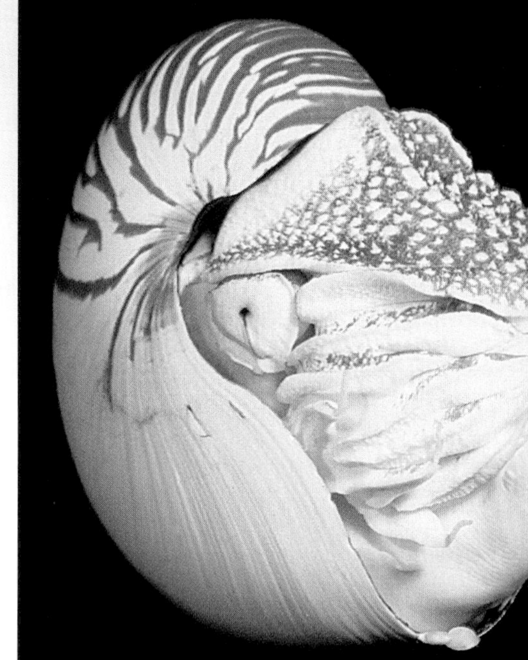

Many squids are able to emit light. Often, however, the appearance of glowing is created by mirror-like cells in the skin which reflect light.

The flame-like markings which decorate the outside of nautilus shells have been polished off this specimen to display the pearly shell material. Collection of live nautilus for their shells has nearly eliminated them from areas where they were once abundant.

NAUTILUS

The chambered nautilus is the only cephalopod that has retained a large external shell. The pearly, spiraled shell has been called the most beautiful shell in the world. The six species of nautilus look almost alike and appear identical to fossils from millions of years ago when their relatives ruled the seas. Several hundred million years ago, before fish, reptiles, or mammals had evolved, there were thousands of species of predatory shelled cephalopods. Today only the chambered nautilus survives, and it is threatened by over-collecting for the shell trade.

The animal creates ever-larger living chambers in the shell as it grows. The older, smaller chambers are filled with gas and body fluids. They provide buoyancy to keep the shell from sinking. The nautilus can regulate its buoyancy by changing the amounts of gas and fluid in the shell chambers. The animal moves around by jet propulsion. Water is forced out of the shell through the funnel, pushing the nautilus in the opposite direction. Prey is captured with the nautilus' 80 to 90 tentacles. Nautiluses are normally found at depths of 165 – 1980' (50 – 600 m) along the edges of reefs. They live longer than other cephalopods, and are the only cephalopods known to reproduce more than once in their lives.

Nautilus typically move slowly, conserving energy, and may be able to survive for weeks on a single meal.

A cross-section of a nautilus shell shows the progressively smaller living chambers, dating back to when the nautilus hatched from the egg. The opening in the middle of each partition is for a fleshy tube, which extends back through all the chambers to move gas and fluid in and out of them for buoyancy control.

The eye of the chambered nautilus is much simpler than the eyes of other cephalopods. It has no lens, and appears to function like a pinhole camera.

Octopus

Octopuses have eight arms covered with suckers. The arms are used for tasting, feeling, and grasping. Most octopuses have no shell. There are about 200 species, which live in various depths of water, from very shallow to depths of 13,200' (4,000 m). Most octopuses crawl on the bottom, but some live in the open ocean. They range in size from ⅔" (1.5 cm) to the giant Pacific octopus, which it is claimed, can achieve an arm span of 30' (9m) and a weight of 550 lbs. (250 kg). Oddly enough, one of the smallest octopuses is the most dangerous. The blue-ring octopus, less than 4" (10 cm) in length, has venom strong enough to easily kill a man. Its beak is so small that the bite might not even be felt. Luckily, these creatures are shy and avoid people. Even giant octopuses avoid humans and pose no danger unless disturbed. They feed on fish, crustaceans, and mollusks, and sometimes each other!

Octopuses, squids, and cuttlefish are masters of disguise. They can change their color, texture, and shape instantaneously. Their skin contains pigment cells of various colors. The cells can be expanded to spread their colors over the skin, or contracted to make the colors disappear. Mirror cells can be used either to intensify the effect of the pigment cells, or to reflect colors from the environment. The skin can be raised up in bumps or smoothed out. In addition, most octopuses can spread out webs between their arms to make themselves appear much larger, or to prevent their prey from escaping between the arms.

THE STRANGEST SALVAGE OPERATION IN HISTORY

A CARGO OF PORCELAIN IN A SHIP AT THE BOTTOM OF JAPAN'S INLAND SEA WAS RECOVERED A CENTURY AFTER THE SINKING ***BY LOWERING OCTOPUSES INTO THE WRECKAGE***

OCTOPUSES LIKE TO CURL UP IN CONFINED SPACES, AND CLUNG FIRMLY TO EACH PORCELAIN BOWL AND VASE AS THEY WERE HAULED BACK TO THE SURFACE (1900)

Bright blue rings appear on the skin of the blue-ring octopus only when it is highly agitated. When not feeding or threatened, it is normally a plain tan-brown color.

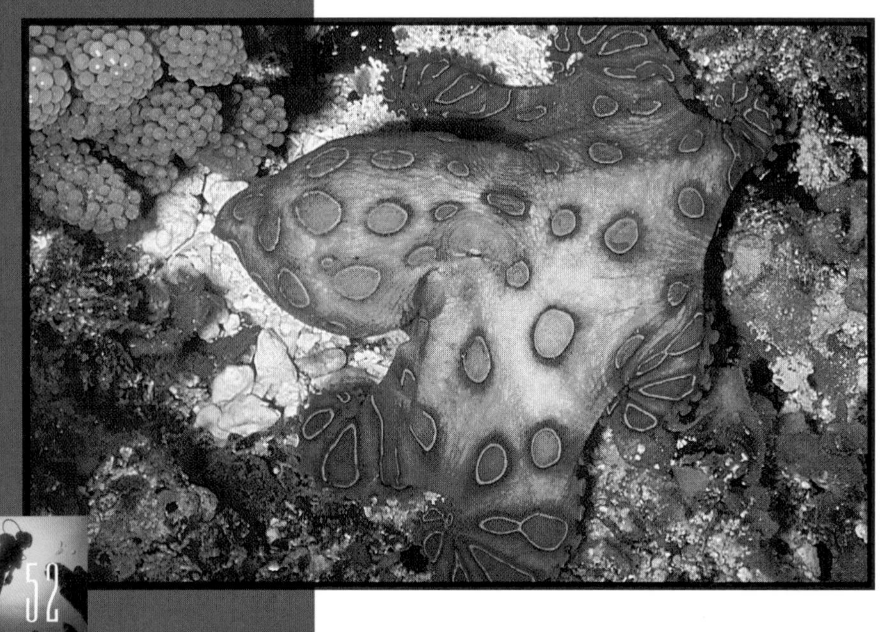

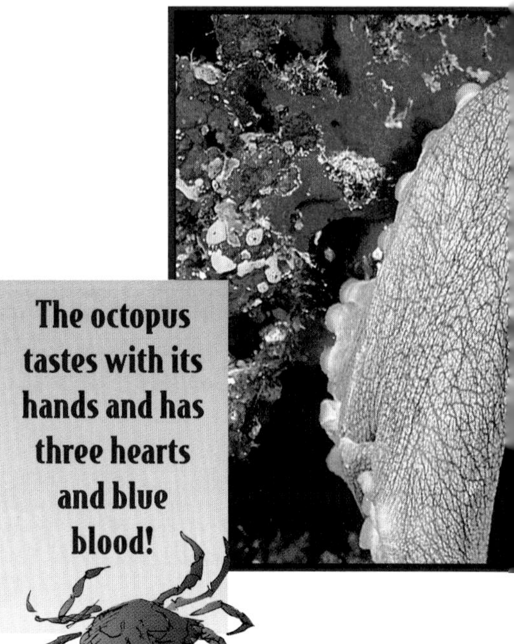

The octopus tastes with its hands and has three hearts and blue blood!

Masters of disguise and illusion, octopuses are able to change their shape, size, texture, and color at will. This octopus has partially expanded the web between its upper arms, but not between its lower arms.

The Stauroteuthis syrtensis, an orange-colored octopus, has suckers on its tentacles that emit light.

With their quick-change disguises, cephalopods can escape predators and ambush prey. A quick color change can make them blend invisibly into the background. They also use "fright disguises" to scare away predators when cornered. Only the firefly squid, however, is believed to have color vision. Other cephalopods only match patterns and shades of dark and light. With their mirror cells, they are able to reflect the colors around them without being able to see what those colors are. Although color-blind, cephalopods can see polarized light, something we need special sunglasses to do. It is not clear what good polarized sunglasses would be underwater, but this ability may help them to determine the direction of the sun, or to see reflective fish better.

Most octopuses, squids, and cuttlefish can escape predators by discharging a cloud of ink, changing color, and darting away quickly. The ink cloud attracts the predator's attention during the escape. It may contain chemicals that irritate or numb the predator's senses. If unable to escape, the octopus may sacrifice an arm that will grow back later. Octopuses use their arms to crawl around the reef, but switch to jet propulsion for quick escapes.

The octopus in these two photos is attempting to allude the photographer by means of an instant color change from nearly white to dark red-brown. The octopus can change color several times in the course of a minute.

Quick, strong, and agile, with highly-developed senses, octopuses are efficient predators and scavengers.

The world's smallest octopus, "Octopus microphyrsus", found off the coast of California, measures only one inch in length!

Mystery creature identified as 500-pound octopus

STOCK ISLAND – The giant eyeball recently found floating in 900 feet of water 26 miles south of Key West was not ripped out of the eyesocket of a giant sea serpent or blown out in the crash landing of an alien spacecraft.

Professor William Trantham, coordinator of Marine Environmental Technology at Florida Keys Community College, revealed Tuesday that the mangled remains discovered by Capt. Geoff Rudolph while fishing for dolphin belonged to Trim octopus gelatus.

He said that the 500-pound octopus gets its "gelatus" name from its translucent appearance. It's seldom seen, noted Trantham, "except in the stomachs of sperm whales."

The charter boat captain and his three clients scooped up the octopus carcass, which consisted of an eyeball, optic nerve, beak and parts of tentacles, including suckers, three inches across.

The local marine professor has been asked to send the octopus parts to Washington because of its rarity. But Trantham said he has decided to keep the specimen for his students and to include in his textbook.

Octopuses appear to have a high degree of intelligence. Experiments show that octopus learn quickly and remember their lessons for a long time. They can also learn by watching each other. In one experiment an octopus was allowed to watch another octopus solve a difficult problem through trial and error. The second octopus was then able to solve it immediately without mistakes.

Octopuses breed only once and die shortly afterward. The male has a special arm, which is used to transfer a packet of sperm to the female. The female does not feed after laying her eggs. She survives only long enough to care for the eggs until they hatch. Giant octopuses may live five years or longer, but most species of octopuses live only a year or two.

Baby octopuses, ready to hatch out lay in egg cases suspended from the ceiling of a reef ledge.

Even the giant Pacific octopus is not able to attack live sharks. This spiny dogfish shark shown here is dead and was scavenged by the octopus. The blood-red color shows the octopus's excitement.

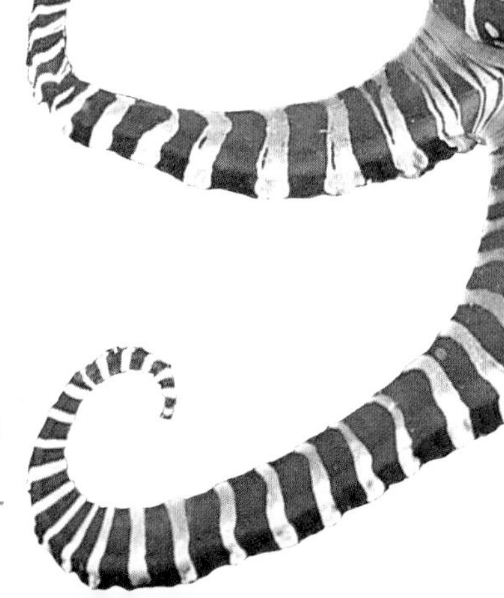

Squid and Cuttlefish

Cuttlefish and squid have eight arms plus two tentacles, which are longer than the arms. Rather than walking on the bottom with their arms, cuttlefish and squid stay afloat when active. Cuttlefish are found only in shallow water, and stay close to the bottom. Squid may be found in all depths of water. They can be found in the open ocean, far from the bottom, as well as close to the bottom, or even buried in bottom sand.

Cuttlefish have an internal skeleton, which holds gas to keep them afloat. This is the "cuttlebone" which is often put in bird cages for birds to chew on. Like the nautilus, they can change the amount of gas and fluid in this structure to control their buoyancy. Squid, however, have only a thin sliver of a skeleton, called a pen. It only serves to stiffen their bodies, and is made of chitin, rather than bone. They achieve buoyancy by adding ammonia, which is lighter than water, to their tissues.

When swimming slowly, cuttlefish and squid ripple the fins that extend from their mantles. To move more quickly they switch to jet propulsion. Squid, being more streamlined than cuttlefish, can move faster. They have been compared to drag racers and torpedoes. They can accelerate much faster than fish, and are able to catch and eat fast-swimming fish like mackerel. Like many octopuses, many squids have venom glands by their beaks, which they use to quickly kill their prey. Some squid have such powerful jets that they can launch themselves clear of the water. "Flying squids" have been reported to glide as far as 165' (50 m) in a single jump.

While most fish can only move forward, squid and cuttlefish can move in any direction and change directions instantly. Their reaction time is improved by giant nerve fibers, which conduct nerve impulses faster than regular nerves. These are the largest nerves in the animal kingdom, and they are often used in medical studies to help understand human nerve diseases.

The structure of the eyes of squids is similar to that of the eyes of vertebrates. However, the photoreceptors, or "rods" in squid eyes face forward, rather than backward, as in human eyes.

The small mimic octopus is able to change its form and color to mimic almost anything in its environment. In this pose it is imitating a brittle star.

The COLOR SEPIA IS OBTAINED FROM THE CUTTLEFISH
THE ANIMAL EXPELS THE FLUID FROM AN "INK-BAG" TO DISCOLOR THE WATER AND CAMOUFLAGE ITS ESCAPE FROM DANGER

The flesh of the cuttlefish makes a perfect pencil eraser. School children in the French Pyrenees used cuttlefish erasers for years.

Water is forced through the funnel of squid (and other cephalopods) for jet propulsion. The funnel can be pointed in any direction to drive the animal in the opposite direction.

The color-changing abilities of squid and cuttlefish are even more incredible than those of octopuses. They can even display moving color patterns, which ripple across their bodies. Cuttlefish are said to "hypnotize" their prey with fast changing color patterns as they approach for the kill. Squid use their color patterns to communicate. They are unable to make sounds, but they can display messages on their bodies. Some scientists believe they may have a simple language composed of body patterns. Males of some species have color pattern "fights" when competing for females. Most squids, however, are color-blind, and unable to see the beauty of their own vivid colors. Nonetheless, their vision is very sharp. At 10 – 16" (25 – 40 cm) across, giant squid have the largest eyes of any animal on earth.

One type of deep-sea squid, *Histioteuthis*, has a left eye that is four times as big as its right one. The left eye is believed to look upward to measure the amount of light coming down from the surface. The smaller right eye is believed to look downward to detect light emitted by living organisms. The right eye is surrounded by light-emitting organs, which may create a beam of light that the squid could use as a searchlight for hunting prey. Many deep-sea squids have light-emitting organs covering the undersides of their bodies. These glow at an intensity that exactly matches the light coming down from the surface. This makes them invisible to predators that hunt by looking upward for dark silhouettes.

The right eye of a giant squid is four times larger than the left eye, and can be as big as a basketball.

Growing up to 13' long, the Pacific jumbo squid is strong enough to snare and drag a diver.

Most cuttlefish and squid, like octopus, can use ink to escape a predator. Some squid have an extra trick: their ink glows, really startling whatever is trying to attack them! The deep-sea squid, *Taningia danae*, which grows to at least 6.6' feet (2 m), has light organs the size and color of lemons on the tips of two of its arms. These are the largest light-emitting organs of any animal on earth. They can be flashed on and off by blinking the "eyelids" which cover them. This "strobe-light" display maybe useful for confusing both predators and prey. In some squids, some of their light organs are found only on males, or only on females, so they may be used to attract the opposite sex.

Most cuttlefish and squid live short lives and only reproduce once before dying. The common market squid, *Loligo opalescens*, found off the shores of California, mate in large groups that attract sharks, rays, and other predators that gorge themselves on the dead and dying squid.

Squid communicate both by color patterns and "body language." The folding of the arms into a "V" is believed to be a threat posture.

The world's smallest cuttlefish is about ⅔ of an inch (1.5 cm) long. By contrast, the giant squid is one of the largest creatures on earth. It is known to reach at least 56' (17 m) in length, but may possibly grow to lengths of 99' (30 m) or more and weights in excess of a ton. We know of these "monsters of the deep" through dead and dying specimens which have been washed up on beaches, specimens taken from the stomachs of sperm whales caught during the era of whaling, and from a few that have been caught in fishing nets. Very few people have ever seen a giant squid alive, and no live ones have ever been filmed, photographed, or examined by a scientist. We know that they live in deep dark water where they are attacked by sperm whales, but we know almost nothing of what they eat, or how they live. Giant squid appear to have fairly soft bodies and may not be very active. They may spend most of their time floating still, waiting to surprise prey in the darkness. Legends of giant squid attacking ships probably come from exaggerated accounts of sick or dying giant squid writhing on the surface.

A baby cuttlefish has just hatched out of its egg case through the small hole near the bottom. A small brush-like patch on the tail is used to cut open the egg case. In the egg case next door, a sibling has not quite reached the end of its 4-month incubation period.

Squid racing is a popular spectator sport in Tokyo, Japan.

Some smaller squids are stronger and more active than giant squid, and still big enough to be very scary. The Pacific jumbo squid can grow to 13.2' (4 m) and can be found at depths of several hundred meters to near the surface. Its strong muscular arms are covered with suckers, with each sucker surrounded by a ring of claws. Its beak is hard and sharp, and shaped like the beak of a parrot, but much larger. Jumbo squid are fast, fearless predators that will attack powerful fish like tunas and sharks and tear them to pieces. They have been known to bite oars and boat hooks in half, and have even attacked scuba divers.

Another type of squid called *Mesonychoteuthis hamiltoni,* found in Antarctic waters, has a body as large as the giant squid, but shorter tentacles. It has heavy muscular arms with hooked claws and a huge beak, and can reach a length of 19.8' (6 m). Like the giant squid, it lives in deep, cold water, and has seldom ever been seen alive by humans.

Scenes like this are probably the figments of sailors' imaginations. Giant squids may grow big enough to wrestle sailing ships, but in reality, they live very deep in the ocean, not near the surface. If, in days gone by, any giant squids were ever actually seen at the ocean's surface, they were most likely dead or dying.

The deep ocean waters contain countless millions of squid. They may be the most numerous large animals on the planet. Scientists are currently aware of about 600 species of cephalopods. The deep sea may well hold other species that have not been discovered yet. With the use of diving submersibles, scientists have only recently obtained the first glimpses of living specimens of animals such as *Vampiroteuthis infernalis.* It is neither a true squid nor an octopus, however, but a weird relative of both which can turn inside out and roll its body into a spiky ball.

Who knows what other bizarre creatures may lie hidden in the depths of the ocean?

Glossary

Algae (plural of alga)– Simple plants that do not produce flowers, fruit, or seeds.

Amoeba– A simple single-celled microorganism that constantly changes its blob-like shape and moves by squeezing out extensions of its body.

Ascidian– A member of the largest group of tunicates, including sea squirts; all are bottom-dwellers.

Bivalve– A two-shelled mollusc, such as a clam or oyster.

Bleaching– A whitening of corals or other marine animals that occurs when they lose the zooxanthellae that give them much of their color; bleaching is a response to stress from environmental factors such as seawater that is too hot, too much sunlight, storms, or other causes.

Buoyancy– The tendency of an object to float or sink.

Camouflage– A disguise that enables an animal to hide itself from predators or prey.

Cephalopods– Members of a class of mollusks in which the foot has been evolutionarily modified to form flexible arms and a siphon; includes octopuses, squids, cuttlefish, argonauts, and nautilus.

Chitin– A substance that is chemically related to sugar, but has a consistency similar to fingernails; it forms the external skeletans of crustaceans and insects, and the internal skeletons of squid.

Cilia (plural of cilium)– Tiny bristle-like structures on living organisms which bend in a coordinated fashion in order to propel the organism through the water, or create currents for feeding, breathing, or other biological functions.

Cloning– Reproduction by creating a genetically identical copy of the parent organism.

Cnidae– Sac-like organs in corals and their relatives, which contain a long coiled tube that can be rapidly turned inside-out and extended to pierce a victim and inject venom.

Cnidarian– An animal possessing cnidae; includes coral, sea jellies, hydroids, anemones, etc.

Co-evolution– The process by which organisms that live together change slowly over time, each adapting to the needs and demands of the other.

Coral head– A structure formed by a colony (or colonies) of coral animals; may resemble a boulder, a set of antlers, or other shapes; may have other animals and plants living on it besides the corals; a number of coral heads together form a coral reef.

Corallimorph– A type of cnidarian also known as a "false coral" which looks like an anemone, but is more closely related to corals.

Crinoids– Members of a class of echinoderms which have a filter-feeding apparatus consisting of feather-like arms which radiate out from the body; the body is supported either on a stalk (sea lilies) or an a set of grasping claws (feather stars).

Ctenophores– Relatives of cnidarians with adhesive prey-capturing cells and plates of fused cilia arranged in rows; most are transparent and planktonic; commonly known as comb jellies.

Echinoderms– Members of a group of marine animals characterized by five-rayed body symmetry, tube feet, and a water vascular ("hydraulic") system.

Ecosystem– A community of living things, together with the environment they live in, all of which interact with each other.

Filter feeder– An animal that obtains its nutrition by straining food particles from the water.

Food web– A way of describing the complex interrelationships between organisms which feed on each other.

Funnel– A short muscular tube near the head of cephalopods, through which water is forced for jet propulsion, and which is also used to eject ink for camouflage; also known as the siphon.

Gills– Organs used for breathing underwater .

Hydraulic– Operated by a fluid under pressure.

Larva– A small immature form of an organism which is greatly different from the adult form.

Medusa– A free-swimming cnidarian, usually shaped like a bell, with the mouth facing down.

Microorganism– A living thing so small that a magnifying device is required to view it.

Nematocyst– Cell found in corals, jellyfish, and hydroids that captures food and defends the animal by an explosive release of a barbed and venomous filament.

Parasite– An animal that lives off another animal by eating its body tissues or fluids, but without killing the animal it feeds from.

Pelagic– Living in the open ocean, not associated with either the coast or the seafloor.

Photosynthesis– The process of converting solar energy into chemical energy stored in carbohydrates (sugars and starches).

Phytoplankton– Tiny plants which drift with ocean currents (from Greek words for "plant" and "wandering").

Plankton– Organisms that are carried around by ocean currents, rather than swimming to determine their course; consists of phytoplankton (plant plankton) and zooplankton (animal plankton); "the plankton" refers to the community of planktonic organisms which feed on each other and interact in other ways.

Planktonic– Drifting; belonging to the plankton.

Planula– A type of larva which is unique to the cnidarians. It is microsopic, sausage-shaped, and covered with cilia.

Polyp– Bottom-dwelling cnidarian, usually shaped like a cylinder, with the mouth facing up.

Radula– A feeding structure unique to mollusks. It is formed of chitin and protein, and shaped like a belt studded with two rows of teeth. It is pulled back and forth to rasp off small particles of food.

Salp– A member of a group of pelagic tunicates with long, jelly-like bodies.

Species– A unique type of organism, individuals of which can only breed successfully with others of the same species.

Spicules– Needle-like supporting structures found in sponges, soft corals, and some other animals; usually formed of calcium (limestone) or silica (glass) compounds.

Tunicates– A group of invertebrate animals that, as larvae, have a hollow nerve cord running along the back, which is strengthened by a stiff rod called a notochord; as adults, most have hollow bodies with a tough outer covering called a tunic.

Upwelling– water flowing upward from deeper parts of the ocean to the surface.

Zoanthids– Small colonial cnidarians, closely related to anemones and corals, that often grow as mats on shallow reefs.

Zooxanthellae– microscopic organisms belonging to the dinoflagellates (which have characteristics of both plants and animals) that are found in the plankton, but also live within the tissues of corals and other animals.

Index

Photo Credits

t=top
tl=top left
tr=top right
tm=top middle
m=middle
ml=middle left
mr=middle right
b=bottom
bl=bottom left
br= bottom right

Corbis
End pages, title page,copyright page, p.i, p.iii, 6 (b), 7 (tl), 7 (tr), 7 (br), 8 (t), 8 (bl), 8 (br), 10 (tr), 14-15 (br), 16 (t), 16 (br), 18 (br), 19 (bl), 20 (b), 32 (b), 33 (tr), 33 (b), 34 (tl), 34 (mr), 34 (b), 35 (t), 37 (t), 38 (t), 38 (b), 39 (bl), 40 (t), 41 (b), 44 (b), 45 (br), 46 (b), 48 (tr), 50 (t), 53 (t), 54 (t), 55 (tl), 56 (tl), 57 (tr) © Corbis

Bob Cranston
Cover, page 9 (t), 10 (tl), 43 (br), 47 (ml) © by Bob Cranston

Jim Christensen
Page 24 (t) © Jim Christensen

FPG International LLD
Page 22 (m) 26 (tl), 39 (br) © David Fleetham
Page 12 (b) © Richard Stockton
Page 25 (br) © Thayer Syme
Page 2-3 (b) © Telegraph Color Library

Innerspace Visions
Page 40 (b), 41 (mr), 42 (b), 52 (b) © Clay Bryce
Cover © Phillip Colla
Page 9 (b), 10 (br), 33 (tl), 37 (m), 48 (bl) © Mark Conlin
Page 56 (bl) © Bob Cranston
Page 40 (mr), 47 (t), 54 (br) © Steve Drogin
Copyright pg. (bl) © Saul Gonor
Page 21 (tl), 34 (tr) © Richard Hermann
Page 23 (tl) © Mako Hirose
Page 31 (bl) © John P. Hoover
Page 20 (mr), 21 (b), 30(tr), 31(tl), 42 (m), 43 (t) © Marilyn Kazmers
Page 22 (t) © Marilyn & Maris Kazmers
Page 7 (mr), 34 (ml) © Greg Ochocki
Page 2-3 (m), 5 (m), 6 (t), 7 (ml), 11 (t), 14 (t), 17 (m), 18 (b), 19 (t), 19 (b), 20 (t), 20 (ml), 21(tm), 24 (m), 26 (b), 27 (b), 28 (tr), 30 (br), 32 (t), 32 (tr), 32 (m), 38 (m), 39 (br), 50 (br), 50 (bl), 51 (m), 53 (bl), 53 (br), 55 (br) © Doug Perrine
Page 51 (bl) © Andre Seale
Page 42 (t), 43 (m), 45 (t), 45 (m), 45 (bl), 47 (mr) © Mark Strickland
Page 3 (mr), 18 (t), 56 (br) © Masa Ushioda
Page iii (b), 11 (b), 26 (m), 27 (t), 28 (b), 37 (bl), 41 (ml) © James D. Watt
Page 9 (m) © David Wrobel

Minden Photos
Cover, page 4 (b), 21 (m), 28 (m), 29 (t), 31 (tr), 35 (b), 36 (bl), 54 (bl), 57 (t) © Fred Bavendam

National Geographic Society
Page 15 (b) © Nick Caloyianis
Page 13 (b), 16-17 (m), 16 (bl) © George Grall

Original Art- Corena Ricks
Page 15, 17, 21, 23, 24, 26, 46, 47, 48, 49, 56, 57

Photodisc
Page 43 (bl), 47 (br), 51 (t), 51 (br) © Photodisc

Ripley's Believe It or Not! Archives
Page i, 21, 46, 48, 60–photographer unknown

Ripley's Believe It or Not! Cartoons
Page 8, 9, 11, 12, 15, 25, 27, 33, 37, 40, 44, 52 by Paul Frehm
Page 23, 29, 36 by Walter Frehm
Page ii, 47, 49, 55 by Robert Ripley
Page 3, 4, 7, 10 by Don Wimmer
Page ii, 25, 49, 52 colorized by Katy Farmer

Marty Snyderman
Page 4-5 (t), 5 (ml), 44 (m), 50(m) © Marty Snyderman

Norbert Wu
Page 5 (b) © 2000 Doug Perrine/www.norbertwu.com
Page 12 (t) © 2000 Peter Parks/www.norbertwu.com
Cover, page 3 (t), 4 (m), 6 (m), 13 (t), 13 (m), 14 (m), 17 (t), 23 (tr), 25 (t), 29 (bl), 31 (br), 33 (mr), 35 (m), 36 (br), 44 (t), 49 (m), 54 (m) © Norbert Wu

In the mid-1930s Robert Ripley displayed this Japanese Spider crab at his famous odditoriums. Some specimens of this crab—the world's biggest crustacean—have been found with a leg span of more than 13' (4m)!